Splat
the Cat

Rob Scotton

Splat the Cat

SCHOLASTIC INC.
New York   Toronto   London   Auckland
Sydney   Mexico City   New Delhi   Hong Kong

Special thanks to Maria.

ISBN-13: 978-0-545-20129-2
ISBN-10: 0-545-20129-2

12 11 10 9 8 7 6 5 4 3   9 10 11 12 13 14/0

Printed in the U.S.A.   08

This edition first printing, September 2009

Typography by Neil Swaab

For Maggie and her very own Splat cats—Spatz and Strawberry.

—R.S.

It was early in the morning
and Splat was wide awake.
Today was his first day at Cat School,
and his tail wiggled wildly with worry.

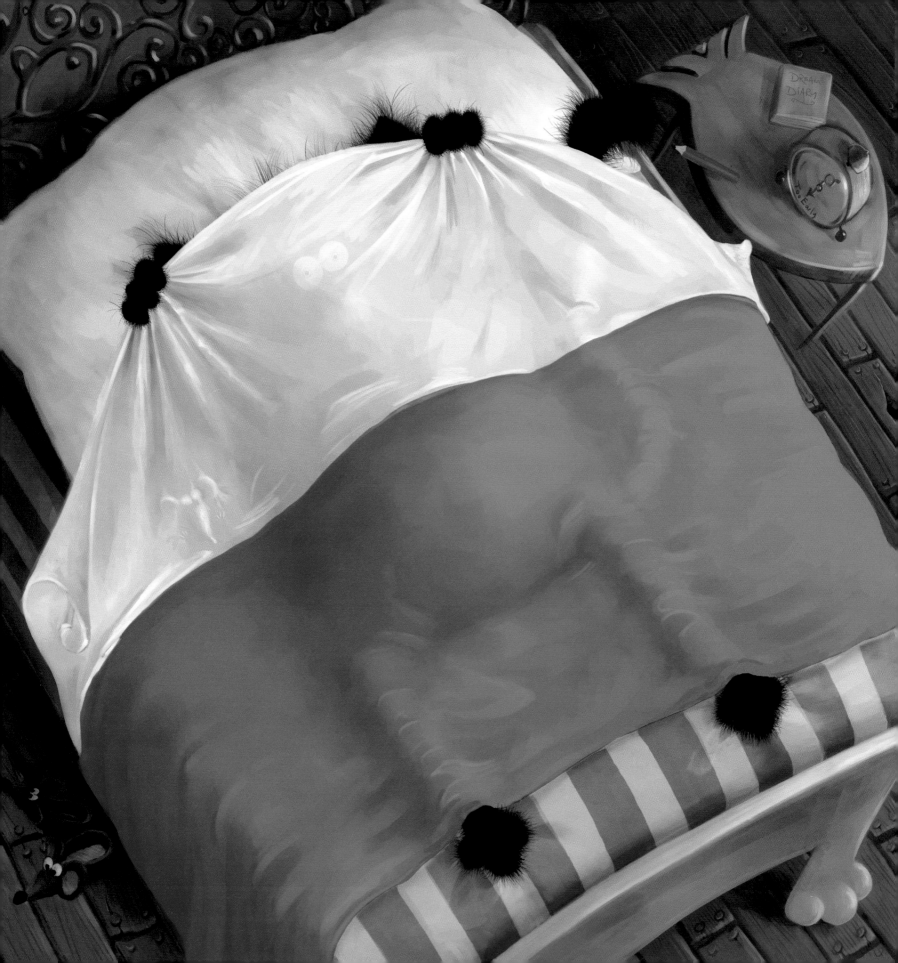

If I hide from the day, maybe it'll go away, he thought.

It didn't go away.

"Time to get up," said his mom.

"Time to get dressed," said his mom.

"I don't have any clean socks, Mom.
Maybe I should go to school tomorrow instead?" said Splat.

"You don't wear socks," said his mom.

"I'm having a bad hair day, Mom. Maybe I should go to school tomorrow instead?" said Splat.

His mom combed his hair. "Purr-fect!" she said.

"Don't forget your lunchbox," said his mom.

I'll need a friend today, thought Splat.

And he dropped his pet mouse, Seymour, into his lunchbox.

"Time to go," said his mom.

"The front door won't let
me out, Mom."

"The gate won't let go
of my fingers, Mom."

"The lamppost won't get
out of my way, Mom."

"MOM!"

"You can ride your bike if you like, Splat," said his mom.

So he did. But he didn't say a single word.

"Welcome to Cat School," said a big, round cat.
"I'm Mrs. Wimpydimple, your teacher."

Splat's mom gave him a hug.
"I'll be back soon," she said.
"You'll be fine."

"Everyone, this is Splat.
Let's welcome him
into our class," said
Mrs. Wimpydimple.

Mrs. Wimpydimple began. "Cats are amazing," she said.

"We're clever, cunning, and quick."

"Am I amazing too?" asked Splat.

"Yes, you too," said Mrs. Wimpydimple.

"Cats climb trees, drink milk, and chase mice," she continued.

"Why do we chase mice?" asked Splat.
"It's what we do," replied Mrs. Wimpydimple.

"Why?" asked Splat.
"Because."

"Why?"

"Why?"   "Why?"

"Why?"

Mrs. Wimpydimple sighed.
"Lunchtime!" she announced.

Splat opened his lunchbox.

"Mouse!"

The cats did what cats do.

Seymour hid behind a glass bottle,

and when the cats saw
his face through the glass,

they screamed and ran away.

Seymour did what
all mice want to do.

"Stop!" cried Splat.

"SPLAT!"

They didn't stop.

"Enough!" Mrs. Wimpydimple said, and it ended. "It's milk time."

"Hurray!"

But the door to the milk cupboard was stuck.
"No milk today," announced Mrs. Wimpydimple.

"AWWWW."

Splat whispered into Seymour's ear.
Seymour nodded and then . . .

A moment later,
the door swung open.

"Yum!"

Mrs. Wimpydimple wrote again on the chalkboard.

Cats don't ^chase mice

"Hurray!" cheered the class.

Soon it was home time.
Splat's mom returned and gave him a hug.

"I've got lots of friends. . . ."

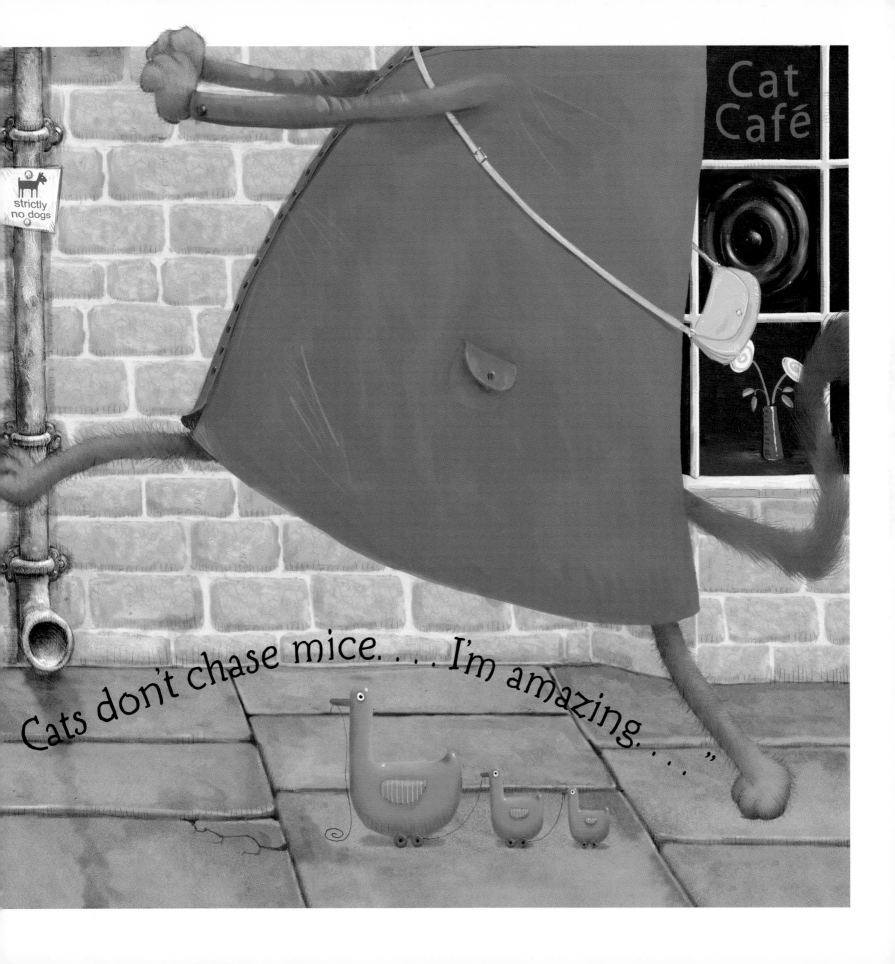

Cats don't chase mice. . . . I'm amazing. . . ."

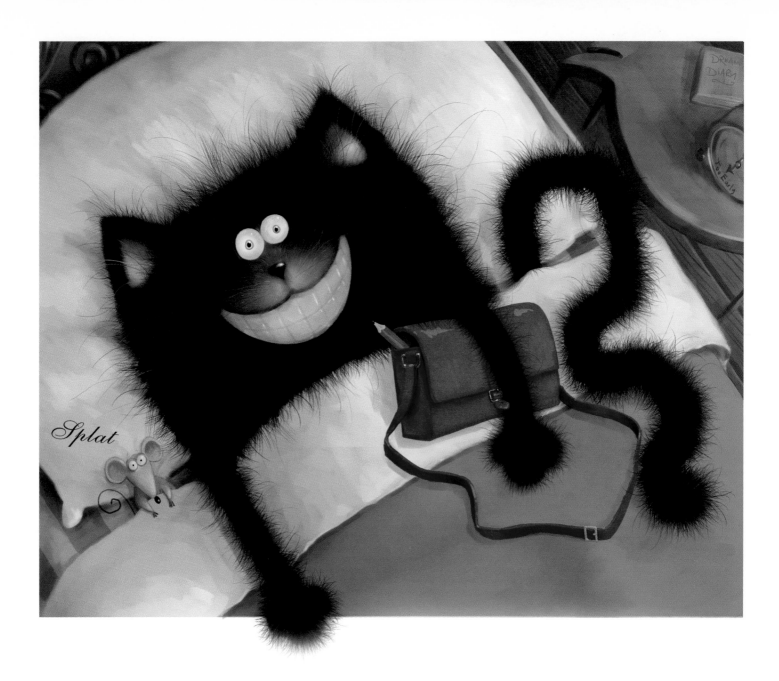

It was early the next morning
and Splat was wide awake.
Today was his second day at Cat School,
and his tail wiggled wildly . . .

. . . with excitement.

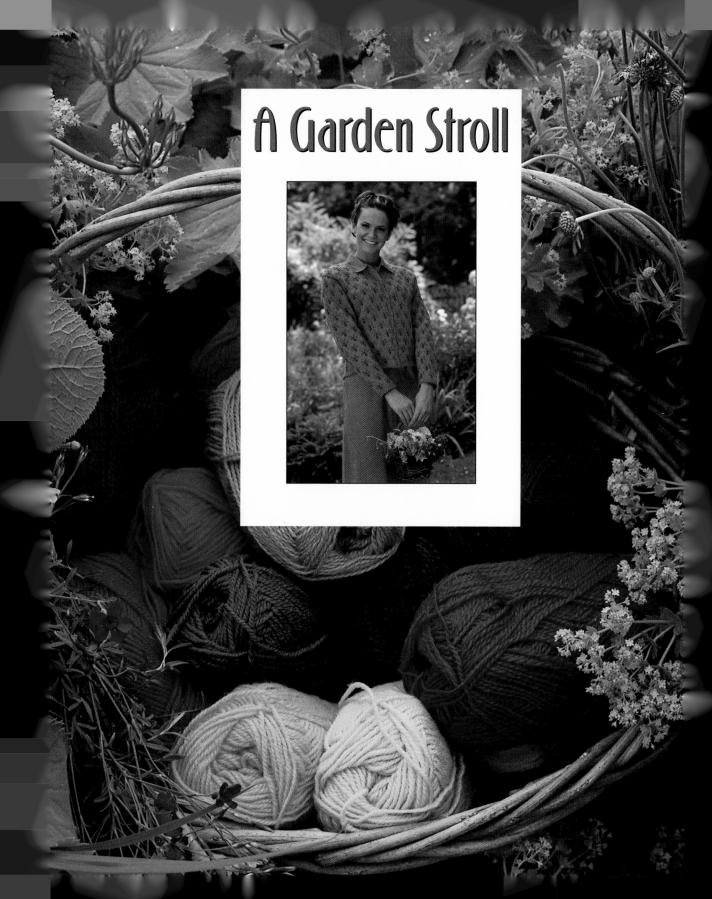

A Garden Stroll

A Garden Stroll

Knits Inspired by Nature

LORI IHNEN

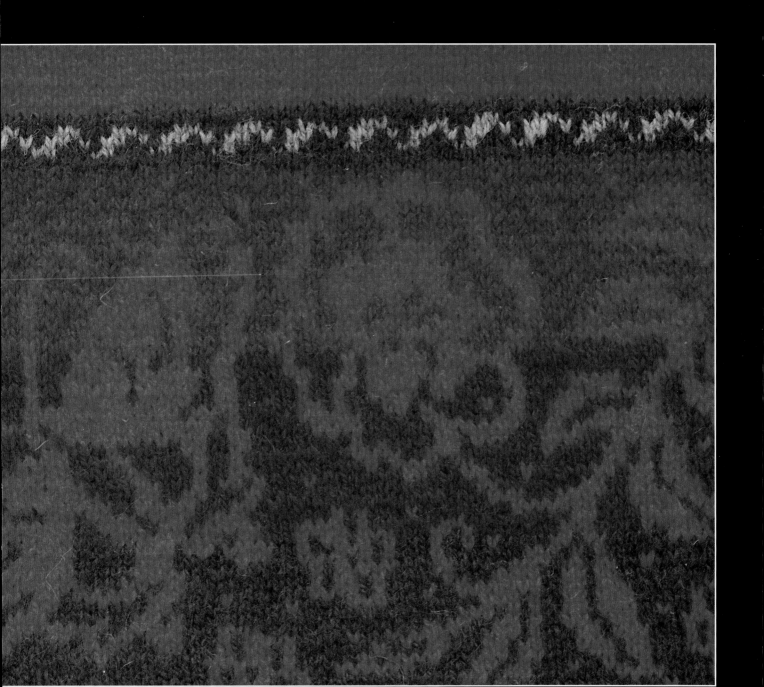

A Garden Stroll: Knits Inspired by Nature
© 2004 by Lori Ihnen

Martingale & Company
20205 144th Avenue NE
Woodinville, WA 98072-8478
www.martingale-pub.com

Printed in China
09 08 07 06 05 04   8 7 6 5 4 3 2 1

Library of Congress Cataloging-in-Publication Data

Ihnen, Lori.
    A garden stroll : knits inspired by nature / Lori Ihnen.
        p. cm.
    ISBN 1-56477-448-1
    1. Knitting—Patterns. 2. Sweaters. 3. Flowers in art.
4. Nature in art. I. Title.
    TT825.I35 2004
    746.43'20432—dc22
                                    2003016704

Credits

President: Nancy J. Martin

CEO: Daniel J. Martin

Publisher: Jane Hamada

Editorial Director: Mary V. Green

Managing Editor: Tina Cook

Technical Editor: Ursula Reikes

Copy Editor: Liz McGehee

Design Director: Stan Green

Illustrator: Robin Strobel

Cover and Text Designer: Stan Green

Fashion Photographer: John Hamel

Photographer Assistant: Troy Schnyder

Fashion Stylist: Susan Huxley

Hair and Makeup: Colleen Kobrick

Garden Photographers: Brent Kane and
Stan Green

Mission Statement

Dedicated to providing quality products
and service to inspire creativity.

Dedication

To Mom, who always encouraged me to create.

And to my children, Christina and Kevin, who patiently waited for me to finish "just one more row," and to my wonderful husband, Keith.

And to Dad—love ya!

Acknowledgments

I wish to thank the many people and companies who have supported and helped me with the making of this book.

First, the yarn companies who supplied the beautiful yarns: Rauma and Hifa yarns supplied by Nordic Fiber Arts; Berroco, Inc.; Dale of Norway; and Haneke Wool Fashions.

Second, the talented knitters and finishers: Evelyn Kindley, Karen B. Lehman, Nancy McCoy, Julie Muehlberg, Astri Olsen, and Lora Steil.

Next, a big thanks to Carol Hazeltine and Debbie Gremlitz for their wisdom and advice.

And finally, to Martingale & Company for giving me the opportunity to make this book!

Contents

Introduction

I cannot remember a time when I was not drawn to color, design, and art.
As a child, I was encouraged by my family to draw and make craft items.
I have always enjoyed designing and making clothing, from my early years
with paper dolls and Barbie, to sewing clothes in high school, to my studies at
the University of Minnesota in costume design (think fashion design, not
theatrical; they are two different disciplines), and now with my knitting.
I have also always enjoyed growing plants indoors as well as outdoors in my
backyard gardens. It is these two loves, knitting and flowers,
which were the inspiration for the sweaters in this book.

I have a tendency to drive people crazy with my love of clothing and especially knitted clothing. I love going to museums and looking at fascinating pieces of art and textiles. As I walk around, I see many things that could be interpreted into knitwear. I have been fortunate to study garments, both old and new, and to have many teachers share their skills and knowledge, from drafting patterns to design application and sketching. I find all aspects very enjoyable and I always look forward to learning new skills or brushing up on old ones.

It seems like knitting is something so basic and yet there are so many different ways to accomplish a similar task. Just think of the many ways people hold onto their yarn and which hand they carry it in. I personally love to do stranded knitting, and I like to knit back and forth. All of the stranded knit patterns in this book are written for back and forth knitting, and one is knit in the round up to the armholes. If this is not your favorite knitting style, you can adapt the pattern to fit your style.

I hope as you look through the following pages that there will be a style, a motif, or a design that will catch your eye and inspire you to make it. If you are looking for a challenging sweater, try the Vines and Birds Pullover (page 67). For a simpler, yet elegant sweater, try Rose Blossom Cardigan (page 81). Or on a smaller scale, try a fun child's sweater and hat and mittens set like Christina's Rose (pages 87 and 93). Whatever the pattern, advanced or easy, a lot of pattern or a little, all the projects in this book are timeless styles.

My Design Process

I have been asked many times how I come up with the designs for my knitwear.

My response is that it all depends on the design you're asking about.

Inspiration for a design can come from a variety of sources:

from old and new fashion magazines, old knitted garments,

museums, architecture, nature, fabrics and textiles, and even dreams. I also cut photos from magazines that I keep in plastic sleeves in three-ring binders. This way, I get rid of the magazine clutter and keep the images I really like. The images in these binders include pictures of flowers, clothing that I like—whether it's the shape, the color, or the graphic image—and examples of color combinations that I particularly like. For example, a photo of a gray rock with some yellow flowers and a deep blue skyline might make a great color combination for a future stranded knit garment. There are also a lot of miscellaneous images that capture my imagination, so I keep them just in case I think I would like to refer to them in the future.

The designs in this book are from an assortment of old ideas and new ones. As you can see, the main theme of my designs is flowers and nature. One of my oldest designs is the Orchid Cardigan, which I designed about 10 years ago after taking a drawing class in which I drew orchids. One of my newest ideas is Butterfly Pullover.

Orchid Cardigan

Butterfly Pullover

Once I get an idea, the design process usually begins with a hand-drawn sketch or a repeat pattern worked up on my computer. When I'm happy with the drawing, I begin to swatch, swatch, swatch until I find yarns that I think will work. Finally, I calculate the gauge and start to knit. Of course, this is the simplified version of my design process; read on for more details.

Sketching

After the initial idea comes the thumbnail sketch. I try to keep all my ideas in a small sketch pad, although I also draw on anything I can find, which then ends up in my three-ring binders. These sketches are done quickly, without worrying about how great they look. It's just a way to keep an idea and not forget it—I'm not trying to be perfect. Out of all these sketches, only a very small proportion ever become garments. On closer examination, some sketches are quickly eliminated because they are unrealistic to make into a knit garment. Maybe they are too complicated or cannot be made into multiple sizes; sometimes they lose their appeal over time because they are too trendy and the trend is over. I try to design with fashion in mind but without being so trendy that you would not want to wear the sweater next year.

Examples of my rough sketches that turned into garments for this book.

Designing with Cutouts

Now that I've picked a design, this is where I can take a couple of different steps. As an example, I'll use the Orchid Cardigan. This design is definitely complicated and has changed some from the initial sketch. One of the first changes I made was to the background. The initial drawing included vertical wavy lines of two or three colors—too complicated. Another change I made was where the flowers ended. At first, the flowers grew onto the sleeves, but this became problematic for multiple sizing.

My next step was to find yarn that had all the colors for the flowers and leaves and to make a swatch so that I could determine the gauge. From there, I could then make a full-size pattern of the sweater outline on grid paper. Then I found a picture of an orchid that I liked and made a line drawing of the shape. With scissors and construction paper, I then cut out all the different flower pieces and taped them together. Now I could place my flowers onto the graphed body and determine exactly where the flowers would be placed.

I made paper cutouts based on the shapes in a photo and then swatched one of the cutout flowers.

One major consideration was where the flowers landed. I did not want the flowers to be too far under the arms, nor did I want them to be exactly across from each other, so I decided to place one of them higher on one front and lower on the other front. I also wanted the fronts to be evenly filled or balanced, so that determined the leaf placement.

I designed asymmetrical balance into the front of the Orchid Cardigan.

Another design element that I wanted for the bottom of the sweater was a lace pattern, so I had to do more swatching before deciding on just the right one. Including a lace pattern also affected the sizing, as the lace repeat had to work into my measurements.

When I was happy with the placement of the paper cutouts, I drew the flowers onto the graphed body. I was careful to make the intarsia knitting (colored design) as easy as it could possibly be by placing the colors in blocked areas. An example would be the red petals that are on the sides of the flowers. On my construction-paper pattern, the top edges of the flowers

ruffled a bit more, so I smoothed them out to save on color changes. This change did not compromise the design and makes for easier intarsia work.

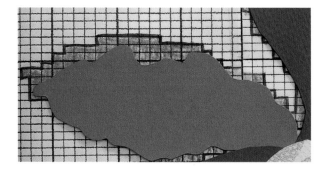

This graph shows the "smoothed out" petal.

I wanted a wavy edge for the bottom of the Orchid Cardigan and made several swatches before choosing the Horseshoe Lace pattern, shown in purple.

18

Designing on an Outline

My Vines and Birds Pullover was worked up in a slightly different manner. I drew the outline of the sweater and the different sizes on a large piece of paper. Then I started drawing the design within the outline, starting with the stems, because I wanted them to cross and curve. Next, I placed some leaves along the vines, and then I started looking at pictures of birds. Some were actual photos and some were from Victorian design books. I had predetermined where I wanted to place the birds, and I knew I wanted one flying and one sitting. I could not find a matching pair, so I drew the heads, wings, and bodies from different birds and came up with my "hybrid." I then finished drawing the leaves and tendrils.

This is the first line drawing of the Vine and Birds Pullover, showing the placement of the vines and the roughly drawn birds. Later, during graphing, the birds' shapes were refined.

20

Vine and Birds Pullover

Designing on a Computer

Another method of creating a design uses a knitting program on a computer. A good example of a design created on the computer is the Traditional Floral Cardigan. I started with a large flower that I liked for the bottom band. First, I did it in black and white and later in color. I then created the flower repeats for the upper portion of the cardigan. The best feature of designing on the computer is that I could quickly make repeats and keep trying different combinations until I found one that I liked. For the upper part, I quickly determined that I needed smaller flower repeats versus larger ones or they would overshadow the larger flowers at the bottom, which is where I wanted the focal point.

In the first three graphs, I worked on the size of the repeat. In the next graph, I worked on the larger lower flower, and in the last graph, I combined the repeats and the larger flower.

Traditional Floral Cardigan

I also designed Garden's Edge Cardigan on the computer. First, I created the small flowers that are clustered on the tall stem. I needed to make the smallest flower as dainty as I could and still have good detail, which is hard to do. The smaller the motif, the less detail you get. To make the large flowers, I added petals around the small flower. This makes the large and small flowers slightly different, yet gives the appearance that they are in the same family. The perfect choice for the bottom border was the smaller flower. Adding some hearts and tendrils is a simple way to fill the spaces between the flowers.

I worked through a number of design options while planning the Garden's Edge Cardigan. Notice how the flowers change shape and position in the different graphs.

Garden's Edge Cardigan

Designing with Three-Dimensional Flowers

Creating three-dimensional flowers is another way I like to incorporate flowers into my designs. Three designs in this book include three-dimensional flowers: Rose Blossom, Christina's Rose, and Flowers in a Row.

The flower design used on Rose Blossom and Christina's Rose is an old design that I have always liked but have waited to use until I had the perfect opportunity. I love the look of crochet flowers, but I knew I could figure out a way to make a knitted one. I wanted the flower to have points and I wanted to knit it from the bottom up. While it took a little experimenting, I finally came up with the perfect flower shape. Putting two different-colored flower shapes together made a more colorful and interesting flower, as in Rose Blossom. In Christina's Rose, I made the flowers all one color. I also did not want the flowers to get too big, so I made them in cotton yarn. The cotton flowers on top of the wool sweater added texture, interest, and more definition.

The flowers in Flowers in a Row came from my sewing background of making wedding dresses and special-occasion clothing. I have made many fabric-coiled flowers and thought they could easily be interpreted in yarn. The multicolored yarn I used gives the flowers added dimension.

One thing to keep in mind when designing a sweater that includes three-dimensional flowers is placement. Do not place flowers where they might be uncomfortable, such as on the back of the sweater. Also, for obvious reasons, do not place them too close to the bust area. On a child's sweater, it would be okay to use them on the chest, but they shouldn't be centered over a child's breast.

Christina's Rose Pullover (right),
Flowers in a Row Cardigan
(below left), Rose Blossom
Cardigan (below right)

Making Color Choices

One of the most important elements of the design process is choosing the colors. To help me decide on just the right color combination, I made many swatches. For some designs, the colors were easy to choose, especially if the design only called for two colors. With two colors, the hard part is deciding which colorway is

I worked a long time on developing the colorway for the Flowers and Bugs Cardigan. This is the order in which I swatched (left to right and top to bottom), working on both color and flower shape. Eventually, I changed to pink and made only one swatch. Then I knew it was right.

my favorite or which one is most suitable for that design. In the Vine and Birds Pullover, I always felt that the motif should be green, and when I looked at the color chart for the yarn and found a green-blue and a blue-green, this seemed to be the perfect combination—a strong contrast yet not as stark as black and white would be.

I think the two sweaters I struggled with the most as far as color goes were the Flower and Bugs Cardigan and Viola Cardigan. With the Flower and Bugs Cardigan, I could get the first three bands to work but struggled with the fourth because I did not want to repeat the same colors too soon and there weren't enough colors that matched and showed up against my background colors. After making swatches in many colorways and not being happy with any of them, I decided to totally change the direction in which I was working. I pulled every pink-colored yarn I had (a very girl-like color!). In looking for the perfect companion for the pink, I selected green because the two colors play well against each other; one intensifies the other. I threw in some yellow just to add a little brightness. The dark plum embroidered details finish the garment off well because they add some depth and unify all the bands.

The Viola Cardigan posed a similar problem because I wanted to use many colors in the violas, yet I did not want any one color to stand out any more than another. The solution was to use five different colors for the violas. The duplicate-stitched navy blue centers add depth and make the flowers stand out. Before I stitched the centers, the flowers and the background together looked like bands of color, but once the centers were in, they became flowers. It's amazing what a little color can do.

Viola Cardigan

Designing Edges

Creating interesting edgings is another important element in the design process. Both lace edgings and picot edgings add interest and make a garment soft and feminine. I try to create edgings that will finish a garment with nonrolling edges and also be an integral part of the design. I especially like the soft-looking edge that I created for Garden's Edge Cardigan. I have always loved feather-and-fan lace edging but felt it would be too big an edge and too large a repeat. My edging is based on the feather-and-fan lace design. By simply taking away stitches and then adding stitches, I created a lovely wavy edge. I made the edging much smaller than a traditional feather-and-fan edge, and I did not make the usual eyelet increases, but used closed increases, which I felt worked better with the design.

Wavy Edge on the Garden's Edge Cardigan

Two different versions of picot edge are used in this book. The first one involves making a facing, then making a YO-K2tog row, and later folding the YO-K2tog row and sewing up the facing. The second one is worked on the bind-off row by making increases in a stitch and then binding off these stitches.

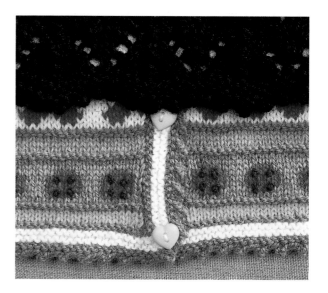

The picot edge on the Orchid Cardigan (top) is worked at the beginning of the garment. The picot edge on the Flowers and Bugs Cardigan (bottom) is worked when the bands are added.

Designing can be a fun and rewarding process. But no matter what you design, I find it's important to first know what you like. Many times, I don't think we always know what that is. For example, I now know I like curved lines and coils as well as pointy shapes, but I didn't realize this for years. It wasn't until I compiled a body of my work, which included items from drawing classes, sewing classes, two- and three-dimensional classes, that I realized most of my best and favorite work incorporated curved, coiled, and pointy shapes. The Vine and Birds Pullover (page 67) is a perfect example of curves and pointy shapes, and this is one of my favorite designs. Look at your favorite things: clothing, art, whatever surrounds you; do you see a particular color or shape emerging? If so, use that as a jumping-off point and be creative.

Flowers and Bugs Cardigan

Orchid Cardigan

Striking orchids worked in intarsia grace the front of this cardigan.

Feminine lace cuffs and a hem with picot edges provide a soft contrast.

Knitted Measurements

Adult Sizes: Small (Medium, Large)
Shown in size Small

Bust: 38 (42, 46)"
Length: 20½ (21½, 23½)"

Materials

- 11 (13, 16) balls Rauma Istra (100% wool; 50g, 102m per ball), color 2036 Black, or other DK-weight yarn
- 1 ball Rauma Strikkegarn (100% wool; 50g, 105m per ball), or other DK-weight yarn, in each of the following colors:
    - 123 Dark Green
    - 145 Light Green
    - 144 Dark Red
    - 124 Light Red
    - 161 Orange
    - 131 Yellow
- Size 2 US (3mm) needles
- Size 3 US (3.25mm) needles or size required to obtain gauge
- Stitch markers
- Stitch holders
- Five buttons, ⅝" diameter

Gauge

24 sts and 34 rows = 4" in plain stockinette stitch and intarsia on size 3 needles

Pattern Stitches

Picot Edge Pattern

Row 1(RS): Knit.

Row 2: Purl.

Row 3: *K2tog, YO; rep from * to last 2 sts, end K2tog. You will lose 1 st.

Rows 4–7: Purl.

Horseshoe Lace Pattern

Multiple of 10 sts + 1

Rows 1 and 3 (WS): Purl.

Row 2: K1, *YO, K3, sl 1, K2tog, psso, K3, YO, K1, rep from * to end.

Row 4: P1, *K1, YO, K2, sl 1, K2tog, psso, K2, YO, K1, P1, rep from * to end.

Rows 5 and 7: K1, *P9, K1, rep from * to end.

Row 6: P1, *K2, YO, K1, sl 1, K2tog, psso, K1, YO, K2, P1, rep from * to end.

Row 8: P1, *K3, YO, sl 1, K2tog, psso, YO, K3, P1, rep from * to end.

Rep these 8 rows.

Back

With size 3 needles and Black, CO 114 (124, 144) sts; leave a long tail to sew the hem. Work 7-row Picot Edge patt. Work first st of every row in St st, work across in Horseshoe Lace patt, work last st of every row in St st. Work patt rep a total of 5 (5, 6) times. On next WS row, evenly inc or dec as follows:

Size Small: Inc 1 st—114 sts.
Size Medium: Inc 3 sts—126 sts.
Size Large: Dec 3 sts—140 sts.

Work in St st until pieces measures 12 (12½, 14)" from YO row of picot edge, ending with completed WS row.

Armhole Shaping

At each edge, BO 3 sts once, 2 sts once, 1 st 1 (1, 2) times—102 (114, 126) sts. Work even until piece measures 20½ (21½, 23½)" from YO row of picot edge, ending with completed WS row.

Shoulder and Neck Shaping

Next row (RS), BO 8 (9, 10) sts, work across 33 (38, 42) sts, BO center 20 (22, 22) sts, finish row. **Turn and work this side first:** At side edge, BO 8 (9, 10) sts once, 8 (9, 11) sts once, and 8 (10, 11) sts twice; AT SAME TIME at neck edge, BO 5 sts, then 4 sts. **On WS, attach yarn at neck edge and work opposite side as follows:** At neck edge, BO 5 sts, then 4 sts; AT SAME TIME at side edge, BO 8 (9, 11) sts once and 8 (10, 11) sts twice.

Left Front

With size 3 needles and Black, CO 56 (66, 76) sts; leave a long tail to sew the hem. Work 7-row Picot Edge patt. Work row 1 of Horseshoe Lace patt. On row 2, K1, work row 2 of lace patt to last 3 sts, PM, P3 at center front. Keep 3 sts at center front in garter st by purling every row, and side edge in St st, work Horseshoe Lace patt a total of 5 (5, 6) times. Place 3 center front edge sts on holder, work across rem sts, evenly inc or dec as follows:

Size Small: Inc 3 sts—55 sts (does not include 3 sts on holder).

Size Medium: Dec 2 sts—61 sts (does not include 3 sts on holder).

Size Large: Dec 4 sts—68 sts (does not include 3 sts on holder).

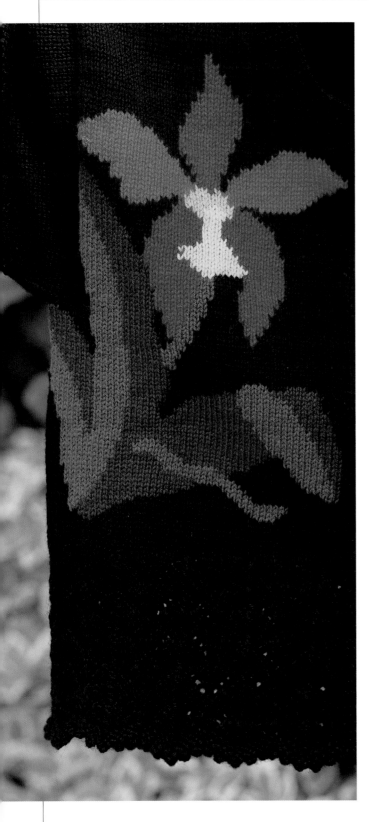

The Horseshoe Lace Pattern adds a lovely design element to this striking sweater.

Follow left front chart for color changes and shaping. Chart does not include center 3 sts that are on holder. These 3 sts will be worked up later in the band.

Right Front

Work as for left front, reversing 3 center sts in lace, then follow right front chart.

Sleeves (Make 2)

With size 3 needles and Black, CO 54 sts; leave a long tail to sew the hem. Work 7-row Picot Edge patt. Keeping first and last st of every row in St st, work Horseshoe Lace patt a total of 2 times. Beg St st and AT SAME TIME inc 1 st at each edge every 5 rows 25 (28, 31) times— 103 (109, 115) sts. Work even until piece measures 19½ (21, 21)" from YO row of picot edge, ending with completed WS row.

Cap Shaping
At each side, BO 3 sts once, 2 sts once, 1 st 1 (1, 2) times. BO rem 134 (147, 145) sts.

Finishing

Fold picot edge at YO row and sew hem in place. Block pieces to measurements. Sew side and shoulder seams.

Collar
With size 2 needles and Black, PU 30 sts on right front, 45 (45, 47) sts across back, 30 sts on left front—105 (105, 107) sts. Work in K1, P1 rib for 1". BO in patt.

Left Band

With size 2 needles and Black, start at collar and PU 87 (91, 95) sts. On next row (WS), place 1 st from holder on needle, P2tog tbl, (K1, P1) to end. Work 1 row of rib. Work rib as established for 1", including 2 sts from holders. PM on band for 5 buttons, evenly spaced, beg ½" from top and ending ¼" from bottom.

Right Band

Work as for left band except K2tog at bottom edge when knitting from holder. Work buttonholes opposite markers as follows: for each buttonhole, BO 2 sts; on return row, cable cast on 2 sts. Sew on buttons.

Sew sleeve seams. Set sleeves into armholes.

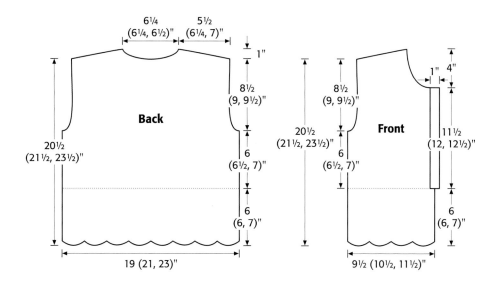

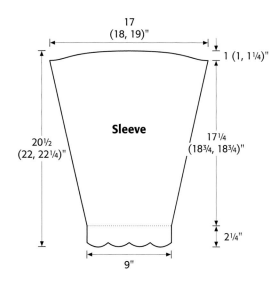

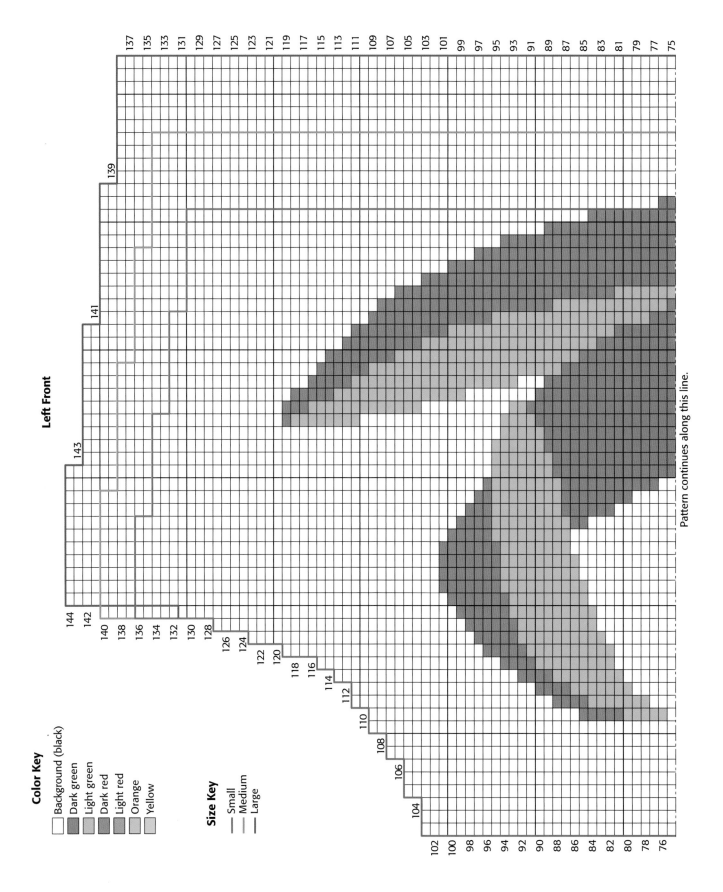

Left Front

Color Key

- Background (black)
- Dark green
- Light green
- Dark red
- Light red
- Orange
- Yellow

Size Key

- Small
- Medium
- Large

Pattern continues along this line.

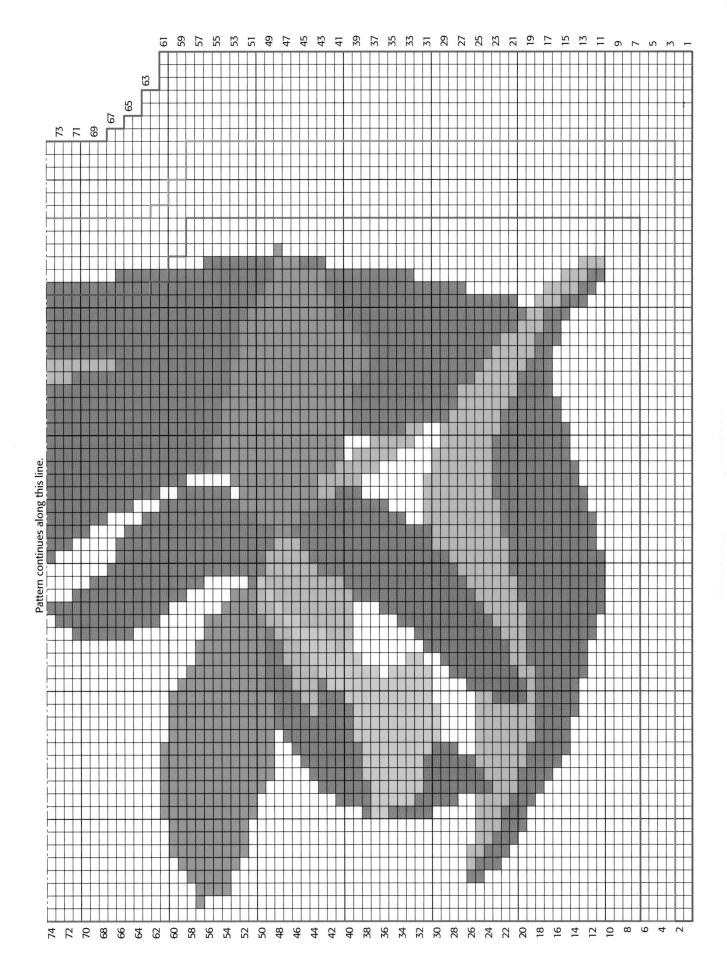

Pattern continues along this line.

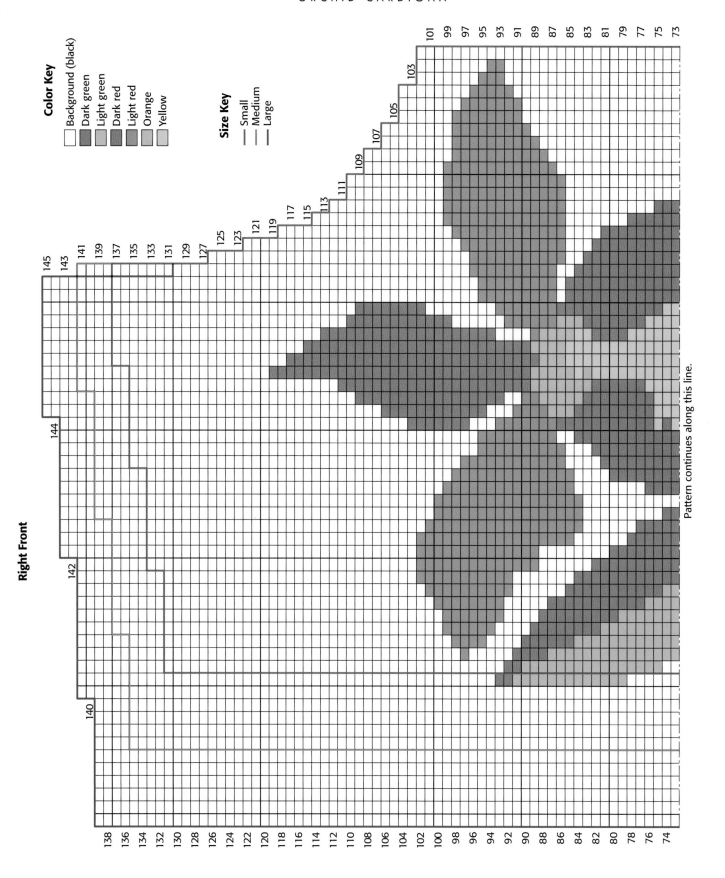

Color Key

Background (black)
Dark green
Light green
Dark red
Light red
Orange
Yellow

Size Key

—— Small
—— Medium
—— Large

Right Front

Pattern continues along this line.

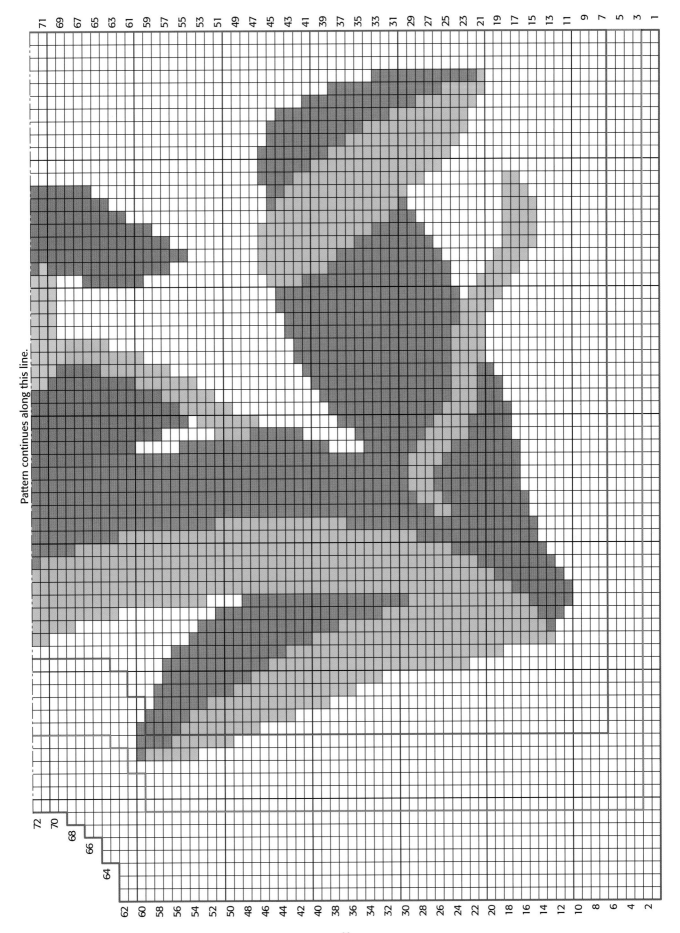

Pattern continues along this line.

Flowers and Bugs Cardigan

This brightly colored child's sweater is a mix of stranded and intarsia knitting.

Picot edges and embroidery add a finishing touch to this sweet sweater.

Knitted Measurements

Girl's Sizes: 4 (6, 8, 10)
Shown in size 4

Chest: 28 (30, 32, 34)"
Length: 14 (15, 16, 17)"

Materials

- Rauma Finullgarn (100% wool; 50g, 180yds), or other 2-ply yarn, in the following amounts and colors:

2 (3, 3, 4) balls	400 White
1 (1, 2, 2) balls	455 Light Green
1 (2, 2, 2) balls	458 Dark Green
1 (1, 1, 1) ball	456 Raspberry
1 (1, 1, 1) ball	465 Pink
1 (1, 1, 1) ball	4886 Dark Fuchsia
1 (1, 1, 1) ball	4686 Light Fuchsia
1 (1, 1, 1) ball	478 Salmon
1 (1, 2, 2) balls	412 Yellow
1 (1, 1, 1) ball	441 Dark Plum

- Size 1 US (2.25mm) circular needle
- Size 2 US (3mm) circular needle or size required to obtain gauge
- Stitch markers
- Stitch holders
- 5 (6, 7, 7) buttons, ½" diameter

Gauge

30 sts and 42½ rows = 4" in stockinette stitch on size 1 needle and in stranded knitting on size 2 needle

29 sts and 39 rows = 4" in stockinette stitch on size 2 needle

NOTE: When reading charts, stranded rows are knit on size 2 needle. Solid color and garter-stitch rows are knit on size 1 needle.

Body

With size 1 needle and Yellow, CO 203 (219, 235, 251) sts. Beg row 1 of chart; AT SAME TIME, PM at side seams as follows: K49 (53, 57, 61) sts, PM, K105 (113, 121, 129) sts, PM, K49 (53, 57, 61) sts. Follow body chart for color changes to beg of armhole, row 82 (87, 92, 97). Place front sts on holders. Working back and forth across back, follow chart for shoulder and neck shaping.

Left Front
Pick up sts from holder and follow left front chart.

Right Front
Pick up sts from holder and follow right front chart.

Sleeves (Make 2)

With size 1 needle and Yellow, CO 49 (51, 51, 53) sts. Starting at point marked on chart, knit rows 1–20. Change to White, and size 2 needles, beg in St st, and AT SAME TIME, inc 1 st at each side every 7 (7, 6, 6) rows 15 (18, 21, 24) times—79 (87, 93, 101) sts. When piece measures 9 (10, 11, 12½)", work butterfly at center of upper portion of sleeve in intarsia. Work even until piece measures 12½ (13½, 14½, 16)". BO all sts.

Finishing

Block pieces to measurements. With Dark Plum and referring to embroidery guide, make French knots, duplicate sts (see page 56), and long sts. Sew shoulder seams.

Body Bands

With RS facing, size 1 needle, and Dark Green, start at right front side seam and PU 49 (53, 57, 61) sts along bottom edge, PM, PU 69 (75, 79, 85) sts up front edge, PM, PU 38 (38, 40, 40) sts along right V neck, 42 (42, 44, 44) sts across back neck, 38 (38, 40, 40) sts along left V neck, PM, PU 69 (75, 79, 85) sts down left front edge, PM, PU 49 (53, 57, 61) sts along left bottom edge and 103 (110, 118, 128) sts along back edge—457 (484, 514, 544) sts. PM on right front for 5 (6, 7, 7) buttons with first and last button placed at bottom corner marker and V-neck marker.

TIP: The band is much easier to knit with three circular needles, but can be done on one. If using just one needle, mark your buttonholes before picking up stitches because it is difficult to spread the work out when all the stitches are on one needle.

NOTE: Band is knit in the round in garter st (knit 1 row, purl 1 row). On all knit rows, make inc using thumb cast on (see page 123) as follows: At V neck, inc 1 st at marker; at bottom edge marker, the st on front edge becomes corner st; inc 1 st on *each* side of corner st.

With Dark Green, purl 1 row. Change to White, knit 1 row, purl 1 row. On next knit row, work 5 (6, 7, 7) buttonholes at markers by working YO, K2tog. Purl 1 row. Change to Dark Green, knit 1 row, purl 1 row. On next knit row, work picot edge as follows: BO 3 sts, *put st back on left-hand needle, cable cast on 2 sts, change to: sl the second and third sts over the first, sl rem st back to right-hand needle, BO 3 sts; rep from * to end.

Sleeve Bands

With RS facing and Dark Green, PU 48 (50, 50, 52) sts, knit 1 row. Change to White, knit 4 rows. Change to Dark Green, knit 2 rows. Work picot edge as for body band.

Sew sleeve seams. Set sleeves into armholes. Sew on buttons.

Butterfly Flight Path

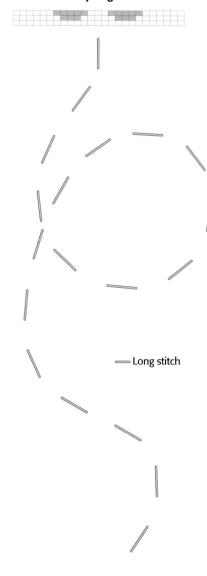

—Long stitch

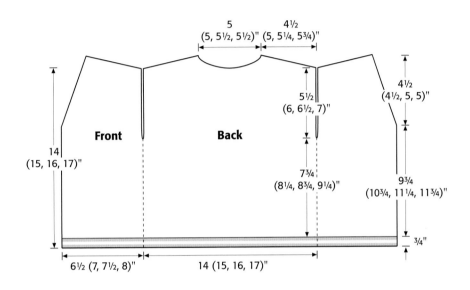

5
(5, 5½, 5½)"

4½
(5, 5¼, 5¾)"

Front

Back

14
(15, 16, 17)"

5½
(6, 6½, 7)"

4½
(4½, 5, 5)"

7¾
(8¼, 8¾, 9¼)"

9¾
(10¾, 11¼, 11¾)"

¾"

6½ (7, 7½, 8)"

14 (15, 16, 17)"

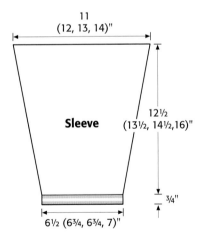

11
(12, 13, 14)"

Sleeve

12½
(13½, 14½,16)"

¾"

6½ (6¾, 6¾, 7)"

Bands are added after body
and sleeves are completed.

Color Key

White
Light green
Dark green
Raspberry
Pink

Dark fuchsia
Light fuchsia
Salmon
Yellow
Dark plum

Stitch Key

Stockinette stitch
(K on RS, P on WS)

P on RS, K on WS
(Dark green only)

Sleeve Butterfly

Sleeve

Back

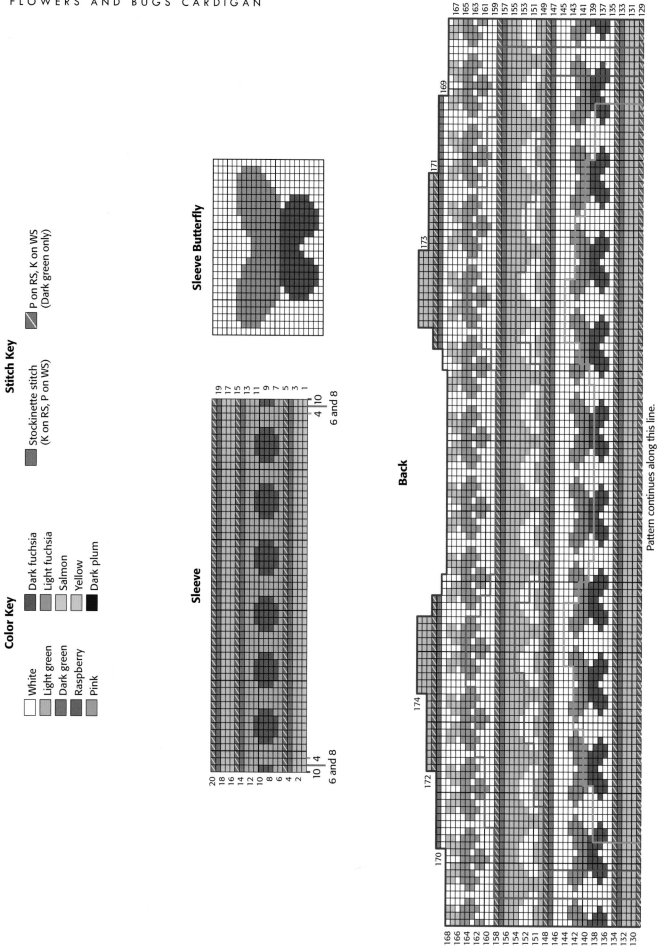

Pattern continues along this line.

Pattern continues along this line.

Embroidery Guide

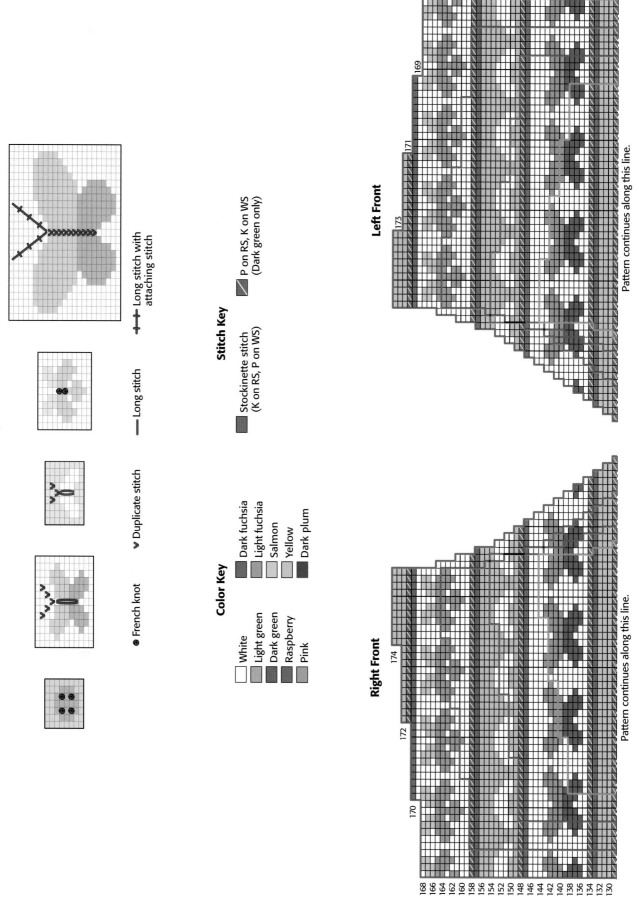

— Long stitch with attaching stitch

— Long stitch

● French knot

⌄ Duplicate stitch

Stitch Key

■ Stockinette stitch (K on RS, P on WS)

▨ P on RS, K on WS (Dark green only)

Color Key

□ White
■ Light green
■ Dark green
■ Raspberry
■ Pink

■ Dark fuchsia
■ Light fuchsia
■ Salmon
■ Yellow
■ Dark plum

Left Front

Pattern continues along this line.

Right Front

Pattern continues along this line.

50

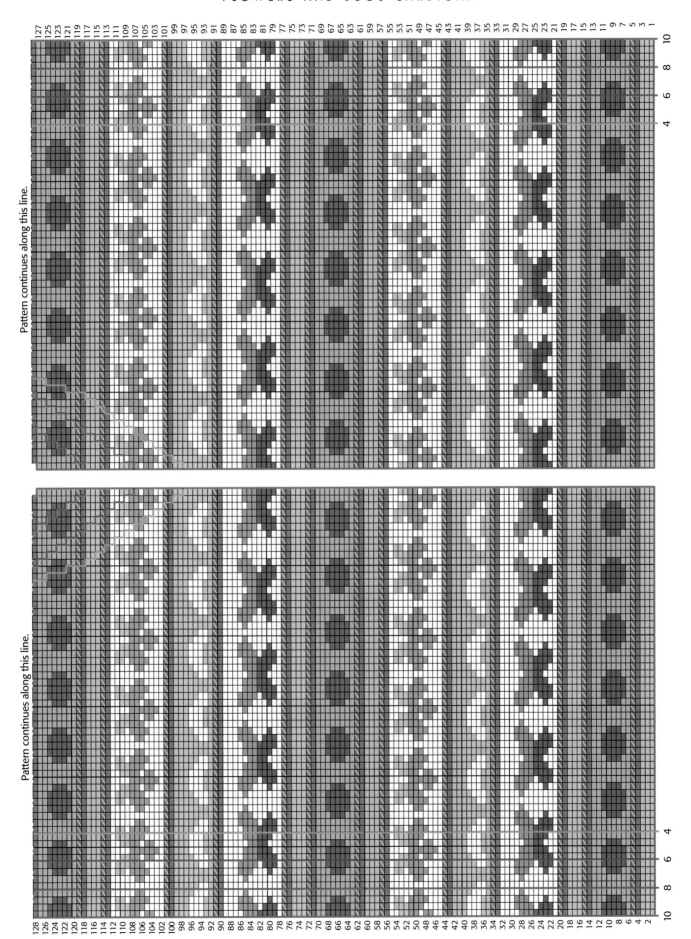

Pattern continues along this line.

Pattern continues along this line.

Viola Cardigan

Multicolored violas dance on a field of blue.

This is an easy pattern to memorize and is finished with a pretty picot edge.

Knitted Measurements

Adult Sizes: Petite (Small, Medium, Large, X-Large)

Shown in size Small

Bust: 33¾ (37½, 41¼, 45, 48½)"
Length: 19¾ (20, 20, 20½, 20½)"

Materials

- Rauma Finullgarn (100% wool; 50g, 180yds per ball), or other 2-ply yarn, in the following amounts and colors:

7 (8, 9, 10, 10) balls	4385 Periwinkle Blue
2 (3, 3, 3, 3) balls	418 Red
1 (2, 2, 2, 2) balls	496 Purple
1 (2, 2, 2, 2) balls	499 Cinnamon
1 (2, 2, 2, 2) balls	4886 Fuchsia
1 (2, 2, 2, 2) balls	456 Raspberry
1 (2, 2, 2, 2) balls	459 Navy

- Size 1 US (2.5mm) circular needle
- Size 2 US (3mm) circular needle or size required to obtain gauge
- Stitch holders
- Stitch markers
- 6 buttons, ½" diameter

Gauge

30 sts and 37 rows = 4" in stranded knitting on size 2 needle

Alternate Colorway

Use 498 Bright Green instead of 4385 Periwinkle Blue; all other colors are the same.

Body

To allow for easier stranded knitting, the navy flower centers are duplicate stitched later. With size 2 needle and Periwinkle Blue, CO 253 (281, 309, 337, 365) sts. Work from chart for 10¾", ending with completed WS row and ideally on row 20.

Armhole Shaping

Next row (RS), cont in patt, K61 (68, 75, 82, 89) sts and place on holder, BO 5 sts, K121 (135, 149, 163, 177) sts, BO 5 sts, K61 (68, 75, 82, 89) sts and place on holder. Cont back armhole shaping as follows: Starting on WS, at beg of each row, BO 2 sts 2 (2, 4, 6, 10) times, 1 st 4 (8, 12, 14, 12) times—113 (123, 129, 137, 145) sts. Work even until armhole measures 8¼ (8½, 8½, 9, 9)", ending with completed WS row.

Shoulder and Neck Shaping

Next row (RS), BO 8 (9, 10, 11, 11) sts, work across 34 (36, 38, 41, 43) sts, BO center 29 (33, 33, 33, 37) sts, finish row. **Turn and work this side first.** At side edge, BO 8 (9, 10, 11, 11) sts twice, 9 (9, 10, 11, 12) sts once, and 9 (10, 10, 11, 12) sts once; AT SAME TIME at neck edge, BO 4 sts twice. **On WS, attach yarn at neck edge and work opposite side as follows:** At neck edge, BO 4 sts twice; AT SAME TIME at side edge, BO 8 (9, 10, 11, 11) sts once, 9 (9, 10, 11, 12) sts once, and 9 (10, 10, 11, 12) sts once.

Left Front

Next row (WS), work in patt as established and cont armhole shaping as follows: At side edge, BO 2 sts 1 (1, 2, 3, 5) times, and 1 st 2 (4, 6, 7, 6) times—57 (62, 65, 69, 73) sts. Work even until front measures 10¾", ending with completed WS row and ideally on row 19.

V-Neck Shaping

On next RS row, K2tog at neck edge, cont dec at neck edge a total of 23 (25, 25, 25, 27) times—34 (37, 40, 44, 46) sts. Work even until same length as back to shoulder, then shape shoulder as for back.

Right Front

Work as for left front, reversing shaping and working neck dec as SSK.

Sleeves (Make 2)

With size 2 needle and Periwinkle Blue, CO 63 (65, 65, 67, 69) sts. Follow sleeve chart, inc 1 st at each side every 5 rows 14 (18, 15, 32, 23) times, then every 6 rows 14 (11, 14, 0, 8) times—119 (123, 123, 131, 131) sts. Work even until piece measures 18 (18, 18½, 18½, 19)", ending with completed WS row.

Cap Shaping

At each side, BO 3 sts once, 2 sts 1 (1, 2, 3, 5) times, 1 st 2 (4, 6, 7, 6) times, 3 sts twice, 4 sts 3 times, 5 sts 3 (2, 1, 2, 1) times. BO rem 39 (49, 51, 43, 47) sts.

Finishing

Block pieces to measurements. With navy, work a duplicate stitch (see below) for the center two stitches of the violas. Sew shoulders.

Body Bands

With RS facing, size 1 needle, and Periwinkle Blue, start at right front side seam and PU 62 (69, 76, 83, 90) sts along bottom edge, PM, PU 101 sts up right front edge, PM, PU 55 (57, 57, 59, 59) sts along right V neck, 59 (61, 61, 61, 63) sts across back neck, 55 (57, 57, 59, 59) sts along left V neck, PM, PU 101 sts down left front edge, PM, PU 62 (69, 76, 83, 90) sts along left bottom edge, and 127 (140, 153, 168, 182) sts along back edge—622 (655, 682, 715, 745) sts. PM on right front for 6 buttons, with first and last button placed at bottom corner marker and V-neck marker.

TIP: The band is much easier to knit with three circular needles, but can be done on one. If using just one needle, mark your buttonholes before picking up stitches because it is difficult to straighten out the edge on one circular needle.

NOTE: Band is worked in the round in garter st (knit 1 row, purl 1 row). On all knit rows, make inc using thumb cast on as follows: At V-neck marker, inc 1 st, and at bottom marker, the st on front edge becomes corner st, inc 1 st on each side of corner st.

Purl 1 row, knit 1 row, purl 1 row. On next knit row, work 6 buttonholes on band at markers by working YO, K2tog. Purl 1 row, knit 1 row, purl 1 row. Work picot edge as follows: BO 3 sts, *put st back on left-hand needle, cable cast on 2 sts, sl the second and third sts over the first, sl rem st back to right-hand needle, BO 3 sts, rep from * to end.

Sleeve Bands

With RS facing, size 1 needle, and Periwinkle Blue, PU 63 (65, 65, 67, 69) sts along bottom of sleeve, knit 8 rows. Work picot edge as for body.

Sew sleeve seams. Set sleeves into armholes. Sew on buttons.

Duplicate Stitch

Bring the yarn from the back through the center of the st below the first one to be duplicated. *Pass the needle from right to left behind both sides of the st to be duplicated. Insert the needle back into where you came up* and then bring it up into the base of the st that lies directly above the one you just duplicated. Rep from * to *. Weave in ends.

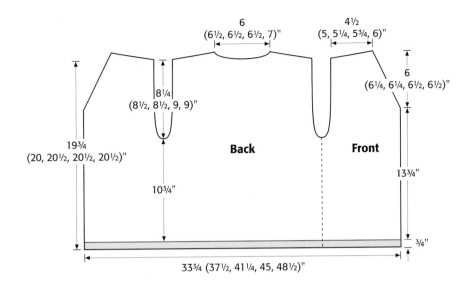

6
(6½, 6½, 6½, 7)"

4½
(5, 5¼, 5¾, 6)"

8¼
(8½, 8½, 9, 9)"

6
(6¼, 6¼, 6½, 6½)"

Back

Front

19¾
(20, 20½, 20½, 20½)"

10¾"

13¾"

¾"

33¾ (37½, 41¼, 45, 48½)"

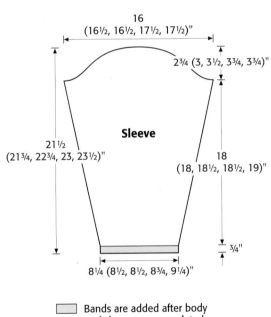

16
(16½, 16½, 17½, 17½)"

2¾ (3, 3½, 3¾, 3¾)"

Sleeve

21½
(21¾, 22¾, 23, 23½)"

18
(18, 18½, 18½, 19)"

¾"

8¼ (8½, 8½, 8¾, 9¼)"

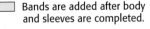 Bands are added after body
and sleeves are completed.

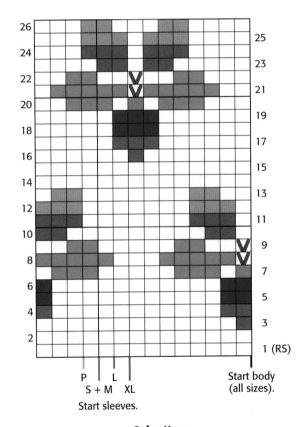

P   L
S + M   XL

Start sleeves.

Start body
(all sizes).

Color Key

☐ Background (Periwinkle)
■ Red
■ Purple
V Navy (duplicate stitch)

■ Cinnamon
■ Fuchsia
■ Raspberry

57

Garden's Edge Cardigan

This Nordic-inspired design includes delicate flowers and a fun, wavy edge.

Knitted Measurements

Adult Sizes: Petite (Small, Medium, Large, X-Large, XX-Large)
Shown in size Medium

Bust: 34 (36, 40, 44, 48, 52)"
Length: 18½ (19, 20, 21, 22, 23)"

Materials

- Dale of Norway Heilo (100% wool; 50g, 109 yds per ball), or other DK-weight yarn, in the following amounts and colors:

  10 (11, 11, 13, 14, 15) balls   5764
  Dark Blue

  3 (3, 3, 4, 4, 4) balls   5813
  Light Blue

- Size 2 US (3mm) circular needle
- Size 3 US (3.25mm) circular needle or size required to obtain gauge
- Stitch markers
- Stitch holders
- 7 (7, 7, 8, 8, 8) buttons, ⅝" diameter

Gauge

27 sts and 29½ rows = 4" in stranded knitting on size 3 needle

27 sts and 36 rows = 4" in plain stockinette stitch on size 2 needle

Wave Edge Pattern

NOTE: Work M1 (inc) using thumb cast on (see page 123).

Row 1 (RS): K2tog tbl, *K1, M1, K1, M1, K1, K3tog tbl*, rep from * to *, end last rep with K2tog tbl.

Row 2: Knit.

Rep rows 1 and 2 once more.

NOTE: Stranded areas of the body are knit on size 3 needle and plain St st areas are knit on size 2 needle. Row 101 is where the change in needle size occurs, and the flower tops are knit in a combination of stranded knitting and intarsia.

Body

With size 2 needle and Light Blue, cable cast on 247 (259, 289, 319, 349, 379) sts. Change to Dark Blue, knit 2 rows. Next row (RS), work 4 rows of Wave Edge patt. Change to size 3 needle, evenly dec 20 (20, 22, 24, 26, 28) sts across row—227 (239, 267, 295, 323, 351) sts. Beg row 1 of back chart (WS row), PM at side seams. Work until piece measures 11¼ (11½, 12, 12½, 13¼, 14¼)", ending with completed WS row.

Armhole Shaping

Cont in patt as established, work across 56 (59, 66, 73, 80, 87) sts and place on holder, BO 3 sts, work across 112 (119, 132, 146, 160, 174) sts, place rem 56 (59, 66, 73, 80, 87) sts on holder. Turn. **Next row (WS), cont back armhole shaping as follows:** At beg of each row, BO 3 sts 1 (1, 3, 3, 5, 7) times, 2 sts 4 (4, 6, 8,

8, 8) times, 1 st 8 (10, 8, 10, 10, 10) times—93 (97, 103, 111, 119, 127) sts. Work even until piece measures 18½ (19, 20, 21, 22, 23)", ending with completed WS row.

Shoulder and Neck Shaping

Next row (RS), BO 9 (9, 10, 10, 11, 12) sts, work across 33 (34, 35, 37, 38, 40) sts, BO center 9 (11, 13, 17, 21, 23) sts, finish row. **Turn and work this side first:** At side edge, BO 9 (9, 10, 10, 11, 12) sts once, 9 (9, 10, 11, 11, 12) sts once, and 9 (10, 10, 11, 12, 13) sts once; AT SAME TIME at neck edge, BO 5 sts 3 times. **On WS, attach yarn at neck edge and work opposite side as follows:** At neck edge, BO 5 sts 3 times; AT SAME TIME at side edge, BO 9 (9, 10, 11, 11, 12) sts once and 9 (10, 10, 11, 12, 13) sts once.

Left Front

Starting on WS row, PU sts from holder and work in patt as established. On next row, cont armhole shaping as follows: At side edge, BO 3 sts 1 (1, 2, 2, 3, 4) times, 2 sts 2 (2, 3, 4, 4, 4) times, and 1 st 4 (5, 4, 5, 5, 5) times—45 (47, 50, 54, 58, 62) sts. Work until piece measures 14½ (15, 16, 17, 18, 19)", ending with completed RS row.

Neck Shaping

At neck edge, BO 3 sts 1 (1, 1, 2, 3, 3) times, 2 sts 2 (3, 4, 4, 4, 4) times, and 1 st 8 (7, 6, 4, 3, 3) times. Then BO 1 st every 4 rows 3 (3, 3, 4, 4, 5) times—27 (28, 30, 32, 34, 37) sts. Work even until same length as back to shoulder, then shape shoulder as for back.

Right Front

Work as for left front, reversing shaping.

Sleeves (Make 2)

With size 2 needle and Light Blue, cable cast on 61 (67, 67, 67, 73, 73) sts. Change to Dark Blue and knit 2 rows. Next row (RS), work 4 rows of Wave Edge patt. Change to size 3 needle and evenly dec 6 sts across row—55 (61, 61, 61, 67, 67) sts. Beg stranded knitting, following cuff chart (row 1 is WS). Change to size 2

needle, work in St st, and inc 1 st at each side 16 (16, 19, 23, 22, 22) times every 6 (7, 6, 5, 5, 5) rows—88 (93, 99, 107, 111, 111) sts. Work until sleeve measures 16¾ (17, 17¼, 17½, 17½, 17½)", ending with a completed WS row.

Cap Shaping

BO 3 sts at beg of next 2 (2, 4, 4, 6, 8) rows, 2 sts at beg of next 4 (4, 6, 8, 8, 8) rows, 1 st at beg of next 8 (10, 8, 10, 10, 10) rows. Work 5 rows even. At each edge, BO 1 st EOR 5 (4, 6, 4, 6, 7) times, then every row 18 (20, 17, 20, 17, 14) times. BO rem 20 (21, 21, 21, 21, 19) sts.

Finishing

Block pieces to measurements. Sew shoulders.

Neckband

With size 2 needle and Light Blue, cable cast on 127 (127, 133, 133, 133, 139) sts. Change to Dark Blue and knit 2 rows. Next row (RS), work 4 rows of Wave Edge patt. Graft live sts to body.

Left Band

With RS facing and Dark Blue, PU 101 (105, 112, 119, 126, 133) sts (including bands). Work K1, P1 rib for ¾". BO in rib. PM on band for 7 (7, 7, 8, 8, 8) buttons, with first and last button ½" from top and bottom edges.

Right Band

Work as for left band, working buttonholes opposite markers as follows: BO 2 sts for each buttonhole; on return row, CO 2 sts.

Sew sleeve seams. Set sleeves into armholes. Sew on buttons.

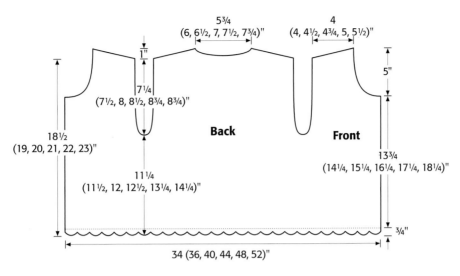

5¾
(6, 6½, 7, 7½, 7¾)"

4
(4, 4½, 4¾, 5, 5½)"

1"

7¼
(7½, 8, 8½, 8¾, 8¾)"

5"

Back

Front

18½
(19, 20, 21, 22, 23)"

13¾
(14¼, 15¼, 16¼, 17¼, 18¼)"

11¼
(11½, 12, 12½, 13¼, 14¼)"

¾"

34 (36, 40, 44, 48, 52)"

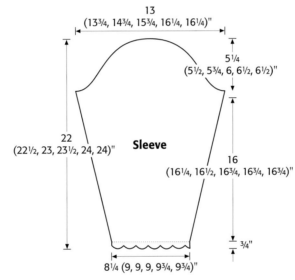

13
(13¾, 14¾, 15¾, 16¼, 16¼)"

5¼
(5½, 5¾, 6, 6½, 6½)"

22
(22½, 23, 23½, 24, 24)"

Sleeve

16
(16¼, 16½, 16¾, 16¾, 16¾)"

¾"

8¼ (9, 9, 9, 9¾, 9¾)"

Cuff

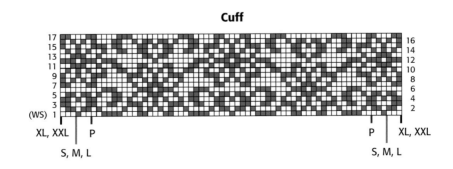

17
15
13
11
9
7
5
3
(WS) 1

16
14
12
10
8
6
4
2

XL, XXL   P   P   XL, XXL

S, M, L   S, M, L

Back

For all sizes, refer to text for shoulder and neck shaping.

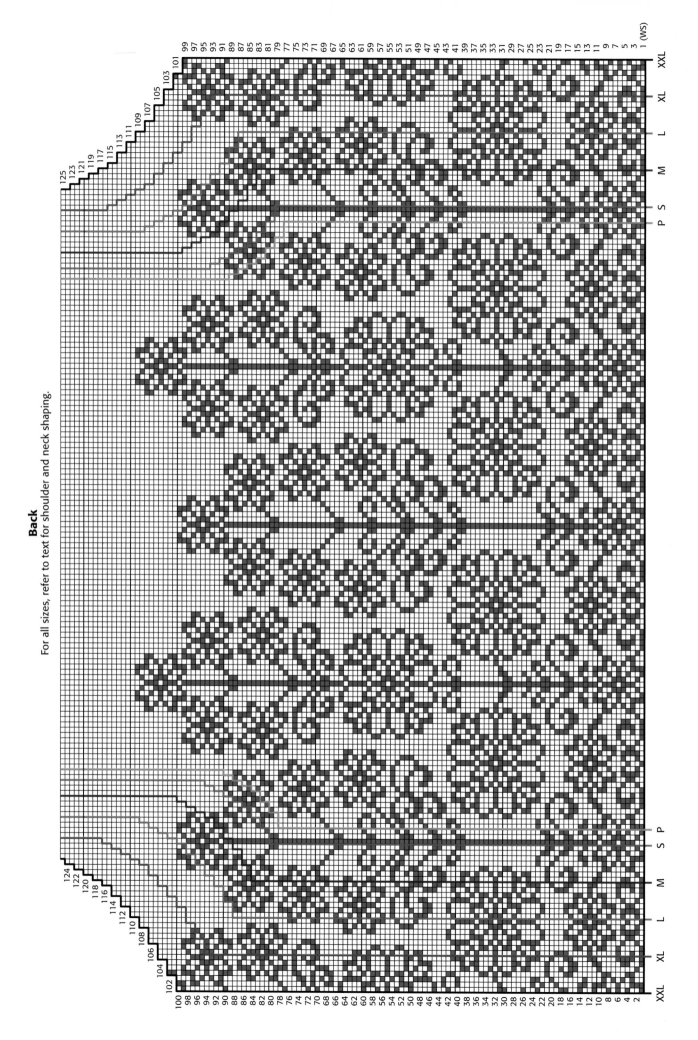

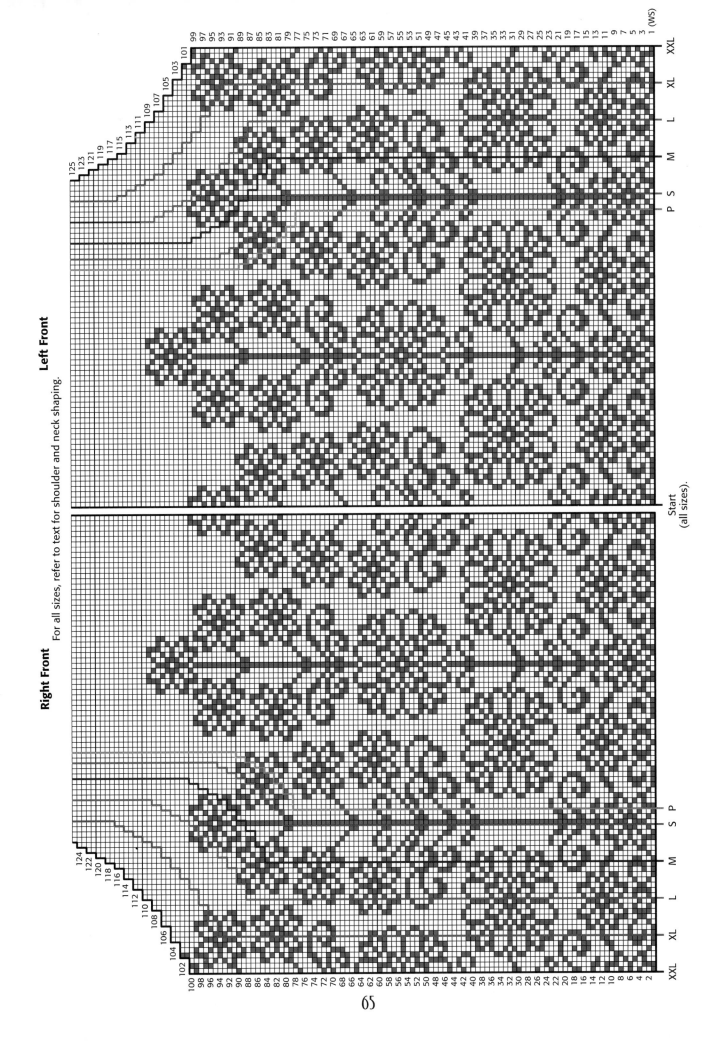

Left Front

For all sizes, refer to text for shoulder and neck shaping.

Right Front

For all sizes, refer to text for shoulder and neck shaping.

Start (all sizes).

65

Vine and Birds Pullover

*This contoured-fit pullover features flowing vines and leaves,
with birds nestled within. Garter-stitch edges provide a nice, crisp finish.*

Knitted Measurements

Adult Sizes: Small (Medium, Large, X-Large)
Shown in size Medium

Bust: 36 (38, 41, 44)"
Length: 24 (25, 26, 27)"

Materials

- Rauma Finullgarn (100% wool; 50g, 180yds per ball), or other 2-ply yarn, in the following amounts and colors:

  | 6 (6, 7, 8) balls | 438 Blue |
  | 5 (5, 6, 6) balls | 483 Green |

- Size 1 US (2.5mm) circular needle
- One set size 1 US (2.5mm) double-pointed needles
- Size 2 US (3mm) circular needle or size required to obtain gauge
- One set size 2 US (3mm) double-pointed needles
- Stitch markers
- Stitch holders

Gauge

33 sts and 35¼ rows = 4" in stranded knitting on size 2 needle

Alternate Colorways

- 476 Dark Green and 498 Bright Green
- 497 Dark Plum and 445 Red
- 406 Tan and 401 Cream

Alternate Colorway Samples

Body

The body is knit in the round to beg of armholes and then knit back and forth.

With size 1 needle and Blue, CO 338 (354, 374, 398) sts. Work in garter st (knit 1 row, purl 1 row) for 1½". Change to size 2 needle. Follow chart for color changes and shaping, PM at side seams. Place front and back center neck sts on holders.

Sleeves (Make 2)

The sleeves are knit in the round until cap shaping, and then knit back and forth.

With size 1 dpn and Blue, CO 70 (72, 74, 74) sts. Work in garter stitch for 1½". Change to size 2 dpn needle. Follow chart for color changes and shaping.

69

Finishing

Sew shoulder seams.

Neckband

With size 1 dpn and Blue, PU 11 sts on right back neck, K45 from back holder, PU 11 sts on left back neck, 23 sts across right front to holder, K25 from holder, PU 23 sts across left front—138 sts. Work in garter st for 1". BO loosely.

Block pieces to measurements. Sew sleeves to body.

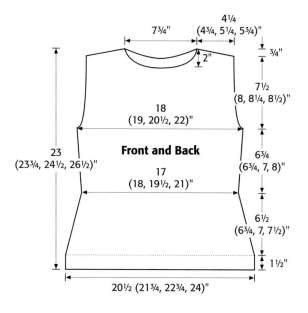

Front and Back

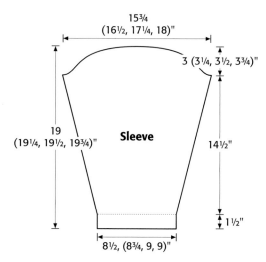

Sleeve

Front and Back

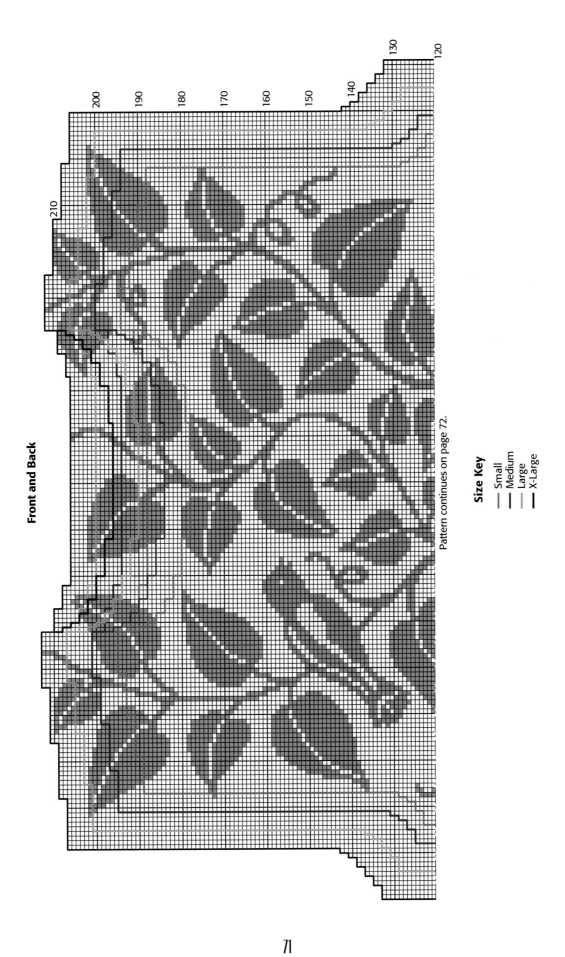

Pattern continues on page 72.

Size Key

— Small
— Medium
— Large
— X-Large

Pattern continues on page 71.

Sleeve

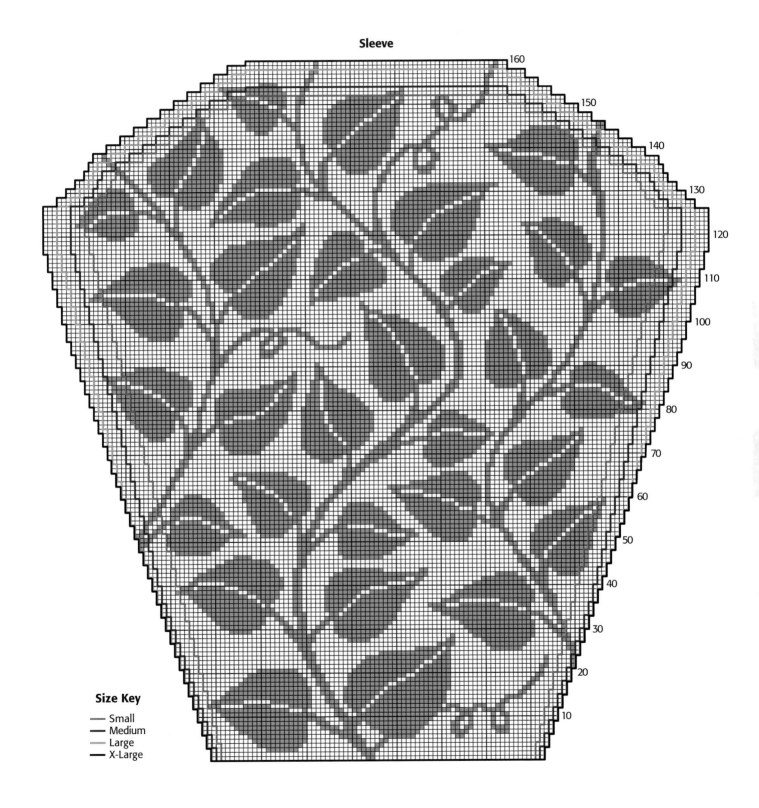

160
150
140
130
120
110
100
90
80
70
60
50
40
30
20
10

Size Key
— Small
— Medium
— Large
— X-Large

Flowers in a Row Cardigan

*This casual-shaped cardigan is adorned with three-dimensional
variegated flowers and seed-stitch edges for a nice finish.*

Knitted Measurements

Adult Sizes: Petite (Small, Medium, Large, X-Large)
Shown in size Medium

Bust: 34 (36, 40, 44, 48)"
Length: 20 (21, 22, 23, 24)"

Materials

- 12 (13, 14, 16, 18) skeins Cotton Twist from Berroco (70% mercerized cotton, 30% rayon; 78g, 85yds per skein), color 8313 Aqua, or other worsted-weight yarn
- 1 skein Cotton Twist from Berroco, color 8462 Variegated Blue
- Size 1 US (2.5mm) needles
- One set size 3 US (3.25mm) double-pointed needles
- Size 4 US (3.5mm) needles
- Size 6 US (4mm) needles or size required to obtain gauge
- Stitch markers
- 5 (6, 6, 6, 7) buttons, ¾" diameter

Gauge

21 sts and 29 rows = 4" in stockinette stitch on size 6 needles

Seed Stitch

Row 1: *K1, P1, rep from * to end.

All other rows: Knit the purl sts and purl the knit sts.

Back

With size 4 needles and Aqua, CO 89 (95, 105, 115, 127) sts. Work in seed st for 1¾". Change to size 6 needles and work in St st until piece measures 11 (11¼, 11¾, 12¼, 13)", ending with completed WS row.

Armhole Shaping

BO 2 (2, 3, 5, 6) sts at beg of next 2 rows, 2 (2, 3, 4, 5) sts at beg of next 2 rows, 2 (2, 3, 3, 3) sts at beg of next 2 rows, 1 (2, 2, 2, 2) sts at beg of next 2 rows, and 1 st at beg of next 2 rows—73 (77, 81, 85, 93) sts. Work even until armhole measures 7¼ (7½, 8, 8½, 8¾)", ending with completed WS row.

Shoulder and Neck Shaping

Next row (RS), BO 5 (6, 6, 7, 7) sts, work across 24 (24, 26, 27, 29) sts, BO center 15 (17, 17, 17, 21) sts, finish row. **Turn and work this side first:** At side edge, BO 5 (6, 6, 7, 7) sts once, 5 (5, 6, 6, 7) sts twice, and 5 (5, 5, 6, 6) sts once; AT SAME TIME at neck edge, BO 3 sts 3 times. **On WS, attach yarn at neck edge and work opposite side as follows:** At neck edge, BO 3 sts 3 times; AT SAME TIME at side edge, BO 5 (5, 6, 6, 7) sts twice and 5 (5, 5, 6, 6) sts once.

Left Front

With size 4 needles and Aqua, CO 42 (45, 50, 55, 60) sts. Work in seed st for 1¾". Change to size 6 needles and work in St st. When same length as back to armhole, shape as for back— 34 (36, 38, 40, 43) sts. Work even until piece measures 13½ (14, 15, 16, 17)", ending with a completed RS row.

Neck Shaping

At neck edge, BO 5 sts once, 2 sts twice, 1 st 5 (6, 6, 6, 7) times—20 (21, 23, 25, 27) sts. Work even until same length as back to shoulder, then shape shoulder as for back.

Right Front

Work as for left front, reversing shaping.

Sleeves (Make 2)

With size 4 needles and Aqua, CO 48 (50, 50, 54, 54) sts. Work in seed st for 1¾". Change to size 6 needles and work in St st, inc 1 st at each side every 10 (9, 7, 7, 6) rows 10 (11, 14, 14, 16) times—68 (72, 78, 82, 86) sts. Work even until piece measures 16¼ (16¾, 17¼, 17¼, 17¼)".

Cap Shaping

BO 2 (2, 3, 5, 6) sts at beg of next 2 rows, 2 (2, 3, 4, 5) sts at beg of next 2 rows, 2 (2, 3, 3, 3) sts at beg of next 2 rows, 1 (2, 2, 2, 2) sts at beg of next 2 rows, and 1 st at beg of next 2 rows.

Work 3 (1, 1, 6, 9) rows even. At each edge, BO 1 st EOR 8 times, then 1 st every row 10 (11, 11, 10, 10) times. BO rem 16 sts.

Finishing

Block pieces to measurements. Sew shoulder seams.

Neckband

With size 4 needles and Aqua, PU 31 sts on right front, 38 (40, 40, 40, 44) sts across back, 31 sts on left front—100 (102, 102, 102, 106) sts. Work 12 rows of seed st. BO in patt.

Left Band

With size 4 needles and Aqua, start at bottom edge and PU 84 (88, 94, 100, 105) sts. Work 12 rows of seed st. BO in patt. PM for 5 (6, 6, 6, 7) buttons, starting ¾" from bottom edge and ending ½" from top.

Right Band

Work as for left band, except on row 6 (RS), work buttonholes opposite markers as follows: BO 2 sts for each buttonhole; on return row, CO 2 sts.

Sew sleeve seams. Set sleeves into armholes. Sew on buttons.

Flowers (Make 4)

SRW(short-row wrap) = Sl 1 st, bring yarn forward, sl st back to left-hand needle.

With size 4 needles and Variegated Blue, cable cast on 50 sts (see page 123).

Row 1: Knit.

Row 2: K40, SRW, turn.

Row 3: K30, SRW, turn.

Row 4: Knit to end (do not catch SRWs; they blend in).

Row 5: With size 1 needles, knit to end.

Cut long tail. Using tapestry needle, transfer sts onto tail and pull to form coil (coil flower so cable cast on turns outward and flower opens); use tail to sew onto body.

Leaves (Make 16)

Work K3tog as follows: Sl 2 tog as if to knit, K1, P2sso.

With size 3 dpn and Variegated Blue, cable cast on 15 sts.

Row 1: K6, K3tog, K6. Divide sts: Put 6 sts on back needle (working yarn comes off these sts) and 7 sts on front needle. Work variation of a 3-needle bind off as follows: *With WS facing (purl side) and yarn between needles, insert needle into stitch on front needle as if to knit and back needle as if to purl, wrap yarn around needle, and pull through both sts and off needles*, rep from * to * once, BO. Rep as established until 2 sts on front needle and 1 st on back needle rem, K3tog. BO last st. Cut 12" tail and pull through. Use tapestry needle to pull tail to back side of leaf and use to sew to garment. Give leaf a good pull to flatten and shape.

I-cord Stem (Make 4)

With size 3 dpn and Variegated Blue, CO 4 sts using thumb cast on (see page 123). Work I-cord for 5" (see page 125). Use tails to attach to body.

Referring to photo, sew flowers, leaves, and stems onto body.

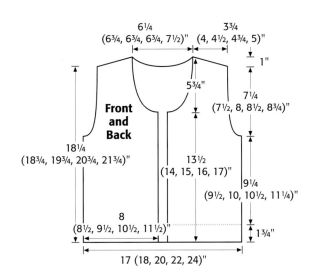

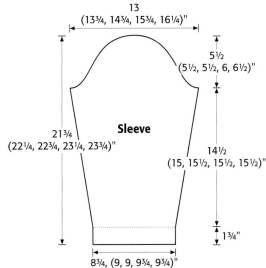

Rose Blossom Cardigan

Luxurious soft alpaca in a flattering silhouette is shaped by changing needle sizes.
Three-dimensional flowers adorn the bell-shaped sleeves.

Knitted Measurements

Adult Sizes: Petite (Small, Medium, Large)
Shown in size Small

Bust: 36 (38, 40, 44)"
Hip: 42 (44½, 47, 51½)"
Length: 17 (17½, 18, 19½)"

Materials

- 12 (14, 16, 19) balls (100% Alpaca Naturals from Haneke; 1.75g, 111yds per ball), color 43 Dark Grey, or other sport-weight yarn
- Hifa Bomullsgarn (100% mercerized cotton; 100g, 227yds per ball), or other fingering weight yarn, in very small amounts of the following colors:
  332 Red
  345 Burgundy
  320 Green
- Size 1 US (2.5mm) circular needle
- Size 2 US (3mm) circular needle or size required to obtain gauge
- Size 3 US (3.25mm) circular needle
- Size 4 US (3.5mm) straight needles
- Stitch holders
- Stitch markers
- 6 (6, 6, 7) buttons, ⅝" diameter

Gauge

Unblocked: 44 sts and 35 rows = 4" in rib stitch on size 2 needle

Blocked: 40 sts and 34 rows = 4" in rib stitch on size 2 needle

NOTE: Alpaca yarn has a tendency to grow in length; also, because the body is knit with a rib stitch, it can grow in width. If trying to decide between sizes, go with the smaller size, as it will grow easily or can be blocked larger with ease.

Rib Stitch

Row 1 (RS): *P3, K2; rep from * to last 3 sts, end P3.

All other rows: Knit the knit sts and purl the purl sts.

Body

With size 3 needle and Dark Grey, CO 358 (378, 398, 438) sts. Work in Rib st for 4 (4, 4½, 4¾)". Change to size 2 needle. Cont as established until piece measures 9¾ (10½, 10¾, 11)", ending with completed WS row.

Armhole Shaping

Work as established across 84 (89, 94, 104) sts and place on holder, BO 10 sts, K170 (180, 190, 210) sts, BO 10 sts, work across rem 84 (89, 94, 104) sts and place on holder. Working on back, attach new yarn, BO 2 sts at beg of next 2 (2, 6, 10) rows, and 1 st at beg of next 12 (12, 8, 4) rows—154 (164, 170, 186) sts. Work even until armhole measures 7¼ (7½, 8, 9¼)", ending with completed WS row.

Neck and Shoulder Shaping

Next row (RS), BO 12 (12, 13, 14) sts, work across 48 (50, 52, 56) sts, BO center 34 (40, 40, 46) sts, finish row. **Turn and work this side first:** At side edge, BO 12 (12, 13, 14) sts once, 11 (12, 13, 14) sts once, 11 (12, 12, 14) sts once, and 11 (11, 12, 13) sts once; AT SAME TIME at neck edge, BO 6 sts once, 5 sts once, and 4 sts once. **On WS, attach yarn at neck edge and work opposite side as follows:** At neck edge, BO 6 sts once, 5 sts once, and 4 sts once;

AT SAME TIME, BO 11 (12, 13, 14) sts once, 11 (12, 12, 14) sts once, and 11 (11, 12, 13) sts once.

Left Front

At armhole edge, BO 2 sts 1 (1, 3, 5) times, and 1 st 6 (6, 4, 2) times—76 (81, 84, 92) sts. Work even until piece measures 12½ (13½, 14¼, 15¾)", ending with completed RS row.

Neck Shaping

At neck edge, BO 2 sts 11 (13, 13, 16) times, 1 st 9 (8, 8, 5) times—45 (47, 50, 55) sts. Work even until same length as back to shoulder, then shape shoulder as for back.

Right Front

Work as for left front, reversing shaping.

Sleeves (Make 2)

With size 3 needle and Dark Grey, CO 68 (73, 78, 83) sts. Work in Rib st for 1". Change to size 2 needle, work as established for 2" more, ending with completed WS row. **Dec row:** K2, *K2tog, SSK, K1*, rep from * to *, end K1—42 (45, 48, 51) sts. Change to size 4 needles, work in St st, and inc 1 st at each side every 5 (5, 5, 4) rows 19 (19, 20, 25) times—80 (83, 88, 101) sts. Work even until piece measures 19¼ (19½, 20, 20½)", ending with completed WS row.

Cap Shaping

BO 5 sts at beg of next 2 rows, 2 sts at beg of next 2 (2, 6, 10) rows, and 1 st at beg of next 12 (12, 8, 4) rows. BO rem 54 (57, 58, 67) sts.

Finishing

Block pieces to measurements. Sew shoulder seams.

Neckbands

With size 1 needle and Dark Grey, PU 100 (108, 114, 126) sts at beg of lower right front, PM, PU 45 (46, 46, 47) sts along right V neck, 52 (56, 56, 60) sts across back, 45 (46, 46, 47) sts along left V neck, and 100 (108, 114, 120) sts along left front—342 (364, 376, 400) sts. PM for 6 (6, 6, 7) buttons on left front, starting ½" down from marker and ½" up from bottom.
Rows 1–6: K1, P1 rib; on row 3 of right front, work buttonholes opposite markers as follows: BO 2 sts for each buttonhole; on return row, CO 2 sts. BO in patt.

Sew sleeve seams. Set sleeves into armholes. Sew on buttons.

Flowers (Make 2 red and 2 burgundy)

With size 3 needle, cable cast on 30 sts; leave tail long enough to attach flowers later. K3, *(turn, K3) 5 times, turn, BO 3 sts, K2*, rep from * to *. On last petal after BO, pull CO tail through last bound-off loop to finish off. Use tails to attach to body.

NOTE: The flower naturally wants to coil inward; sew it down the opposite of its natural coil and the flower will lie open more. Coil 1 red flower and 1 burgundy flower tog; attach to cuffs.

Leaves (Make 4)

NOTE: On rows 3 and 7, knit into back of YO sts.

With size 3 needle and Green, make slipknot, K1, and place on needle—2 sts.

Row 1: K2.

Row 2: K1, YO, K1.

Rows 3, 4, and 5: K3.

Row 6: K1, YO, K1, YO, K1.

Rows 7, 8, 9, 10, and 11: K5.

Row 12: SSK, K1, K2tog.

Row 13: K3.

Row 14: Sl 2tog as if to knit, K1, P2sso.

Cut yarn and pull loop through. To identify RS, note that WS has slants where YOs were knit into back. Use tails to sew down, two per flower.

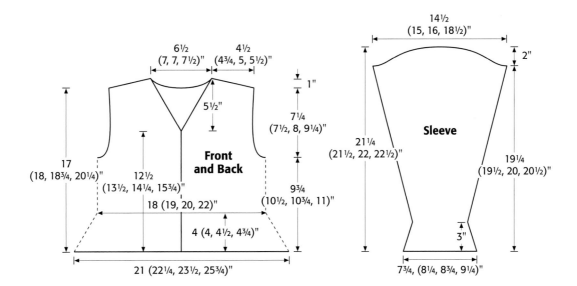

Christina's Rose Pullover

A fun mix of textures, three-dimensional flowers blossoming up the front, and delicate picot edges all work together to create this charming sweater.

Knitted Measurements

Girl's Sizes: 4 (6, 8, 10, 12)

Shown in size 6

Chest: 29 (30, 32, 34, 37)"
Length: 13 (13½, 14½, 15¼, 15¾)"

Materials

- (MC) 3 (4, 4, 5, 5) balls Rauma Finnullgarn (100% wool; 50g, 180yds per ball), color 466 Mauve, or other 2-ply yarn
- (CC) 1 hank Hifa Bomullsgarn (100% mercerized cotton; 100g, 227yds per hank), color 345 Rose, or other fingering-weight yarn
- Size 3 US (3.25mm) needles or size required to obtain gauge
- One set size 3 US (3.25mm) double-pointed needles

Gauge

24½ sts and 36 rows = 4" in stockinette stitch

Picot Edge Pattern

Rows 1–4: Work in St st.

Row 5 (RS): *K2tog, YO; rep from * to last 2 sts, K2tog. You will lose 1 st.

Rows 6 and 8: Purl.

Rows 7, 9, and 10: Knit.

Back

With size 3 needle and CC, cable cast on 88 (92, 98, 104, 114) sts; leave a long tail to sew hem later. Work Picot Edge patt. Change to MC and work in St st until piece measures 7 (7, 7½, 7¾, 8)" from YO-K2tog row.

Armhole Shaping

At each side, BO 3 (3, 4, 4, 4) sts, then 1 st 3 (3, 5, 5, 7) times—75 (79, 79, 85, 91) sts. Work even until armhole measures 6 (6½, 7, 7½, 7¾)", ending with completed WS row.

Shoulder and Neck Shaping

Next row (RS), BO 7 (7, 7, 8, 8) sts, work across 18 (18, 18, 19, 21) sts, BO center 25 (29, 29, 31, 33) sts, finish row. **Turn and work this side first:** At side edge, BO 7 (7, 7, 8, 8) sts twice, 7 (7, 7, 7, 9) sts once; AT SAME TIME at neck edge, BO 2 sts twice. **On WS, attach yarn at neck edge and work opposite side as follows:** At neck edge, BO 2 sts twice; AT SAME TIME at side edge, BO 7 (7, 7, 8, 8) sts once and 7 (7, 7, 7, 9) sts once.

Front

Work as for back, including armhole shaping, until piece measures 11 (11¼, 12¼, 12½, 13)" from YO-K2tog row, ending with completed WS row.

Neck Shaping

Next row (RS), K33 (35, 35, 38, 41) sts, join second ball of yarn and BO center 9 sts, finish row. Working both sides at once, at each neck edge, BO 4 sts once, 3 sts once, 2 sts twice, and 1 st 1 (3, 3, 4, 5) times—21 (21, 21, 23, 25) sts. Work even until same length as back, then shape shoulders as for back.

Sleeves (Make 2)

With size 3 needle and CC, cable cast on 42 (44, 46, 46, 48) sts. Work Picot Edge patt. Change to MC and evenly inc 4 sts while working in St st. Work 1 row even, then inc 1 st at each side every 2 rows 4 times. Inc 1 st at each side every 8 (7, 6, 5, 5) rows 10 (12, 14, 17, 18) times—73 (79, 85, 91, 95) sts. Work even until sleeve measures 12 (13, 13½, 14¼, 14½)" from YO-K2tog row.

Cap Shaping

At each side, BO 3 (3, 4, 4, 4) sts once, then 1 st EOR 3 (3, 5, 5, 7) times. BO rem 61 (67, 67, 73, 73) sts.

Finishing

Block pieces to measurements.

Flowers (Make 5)

With size 3 needle and CC, cable cast on 36 sts; leave tail long enough to attach flowers later. K3, *(turn, K3) 5 times, turn, BO 3 sts, K2*. Rep from * to *; on last petal after BO, pull CO tail through last bound-off loop to finish off. Use tails to attach flowers.

NOTE: The flower naturally wants to coil inward; sew it down the opposite of its natural coiling and the flower will lie open more.

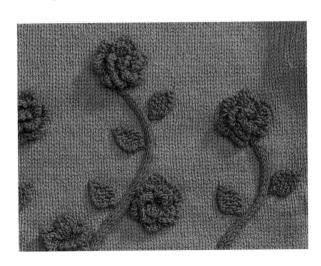

Leaves (Make 13)

NOTE: On rows 3 and 7, knit into back of YO sts.

With size 3 needles and CC, make slipknot, K1, and place on needle—2 sts.

Row 1: K2.

Row 2: K1, YO, K1.

Rows 3, 4, and 5: K3.

Row 6: K1, YO, K1, YO, K1.

Rows 7, 8, 9, 10, and 11: K5.

Row 12: SSK, K1, K2tog.

Row 13: K3.

Row 14: Sl 2tog as if to knit, K1, P2sso.

Cut yarn and pull loop through. To identify RS, note that WS has slants where YOs were knit into back. Use tails to sew leaves. Use CO for leaf tip and BO for stem.

I-Cord Stems

With size 3 needle and CC, CO 4 sts using thumb cast on (see page 123). Work I-cord (see page 125) for 3¼", then at beg of row, K2tog, cont until length is 6½". Make 2. CO 4 sts using thumb cast on. Work I-cord for 4", then dec as above; cont until length is 8". Make 1.

NOTE: These are approx lengths, make them longer or shorter as needed. Use tails to attach I-cords.

Referring to diagram, sew stems, then flowers and leaves to front.

Sew shoulders and sleeve seams. Set sleeves into armholes. Sew bottom hem.

Collar

NOTE: When working in the round, on rows where the purl ridge and YO row need to appear to go straight across (remember the beg of a row jogs upwards when knitting in the round), sl the first st. You can only do this EOR, so it works perfectly to sl the first st on

Flower, Leaf, and Stem Placement

rows 2, 4, and 11. On each of these rows, your first st moves over by one space. Make your inc and dec on rows 5 and 15 as if the original st is still the first st.

With size 3 dpn and CC, start at right back seam and PU 40 (44, 44, 46, 48) sts across back and 54 (60, 60, 70, 74) sts across front—94 (104, 104, 116, 122) sts.

Rows 1 and 3: Purl.

Rows 2, 4, 6–9, and 11–14: Knit.

Row 5: Knit; AT SAME TIME, dec 4 sts evenly across back and 6 (8, 8, 10, 10) sts evenly across front.

Row 10: *K2tog, YO, rep from * to end.

Row 15: Knit; AT SAME TIME, inc 4 sts evenly across back and 6 (8, 8, 10, 10) sts across front to correspond with dec on row 5.

Row 16: BO.

Front and Back

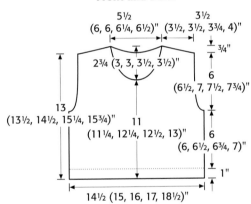

Sleeve

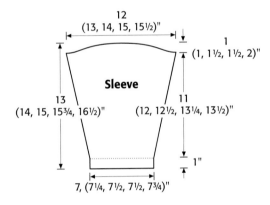

Christina's Rose Hat and Mittens

Knitted Measurements

Girl's Sizes: Small/Medium (Large)
Shown in size Small/Medium

Hat Circumference: 22 (23½)"
Hat Length with Brim Folded Up: 8¼ (9)"
Mitten Circumference above Thumb: 6¾ (7¼)"

Mitten Length: 5½ (6½)"

Materials

- (MC) 2 balls Rauma Finullgarn (100% wool; 50g, 180yds per ball), color 466 Mauve, or other 2-ply yarn
- (CC) 1 hank Hifa Bomullsgarn (100% mercerized cotton; 100g, 227yds per ball), color 345 Rose, or other fingering-weight yarn
- Size 2 US (3mm) needles
- Size 3 US (3.25mm) needles or size required to obtain gauge
- Stitch markers

Gauge

24½ sts and 36 rows = 4" in stockinette stitch on size 3 needles

Hat Body

With size 3 needle and CC, cable cast on 136 (144) sts; leave long tail to sew hem later. Work Picot Edge patt (see page 88). Change to MC. On first row, inc 1 (2) sts. Knit even in St st until piece measures 4¾ (5)" from YO row. Change to reverse St st, work even until piece measures 7¼ (8)" from YO row, ending with completed WS row.

Cap Shaping

Row 1 (RS): K1, *K2tog, K13 (15), rep from * to end.

Rows 2, 3, and 4: Work in St st.

Row 5: K1, *K2tog, K12 (14), rep from * to end.

Rows 6, 7, and 8: Work in St st.

Dec as established 5 (7) times more. Dec on every RS row until 10 sts rem. Purl 1 row. Cut long tail and thread through sts; pull tight. Sew down seam, reversing seam at St st–reverse St st intersection. Use cast-on tail to sew Picot Edge hem.

Finishing

Make 3 flowers and 3 leaves as for sweater (see pages 89–90). Attach to hat brim in a cluster.

Right Mitten

With size 3 needle and CC, cable cast on 48 (52) sts; leave long tail to sew hem later. Work Picot Edge patt (see page 88). Change to MC. Work in St st for 3 (5) rows. Change to size 2 needles; on next row, dec 5 by working P2tog evenly across row—42 (46) sts. Work 6 (8) rows in St st. Change to size 3 needles, work 4 (6) more rows in St st.

Thumb Increases

M1 by pulling up strand of yarn between sts and knit into back of st (see page 125).

Row 1: K21 (23), PM, M1, K2, M1, PM, K19 (21).

Row 2: Purl.

Row 3: K21 (23), M1, K4, M1, K19 (21).

Row 4: Purl.

Row 5: K21 (23), M1, K6, M1, K19 (21).

Row 6: Purl.

Rows 7–14 (7–16): Cont inc as set for a total of 16 (18) sts between markers—56 (58) sts.

Row 15 (17): Work thumb: K37 (41), turn, CO 1 st, P16 (19), turn, CO 1 st, K17 (19).

On these 18 (20) sts, work 7 (11) rows (or to desired thumb length), ending with completed WS row. **Dec row: K2tog 2 (1) times, K3tog 4 (5) times, K2tog 1 time. Cut yarn and thread through rem sts; pull tight and sew thumb seam. With RS facing, PU 3 sts across thumb and complete row 15 (17). Work 19 (27) rows (or to desired length) in St st, ending with completed WS row.

Top Shaping

Row 1(RS): K1, [SSK, K16 (18), K2tog, K1] twice.

Rows 2–4: Work in St st.

Row 5: K1, [SSK, K14 (16), K2tog, K1] twice.

Rows 6 and 8: Purl.

Row 7: K1, [SSK, K12 (14), K2tog, K1] twice.

Row 9: K1, [SSK, K10 (12), K2tog, K1] twice.

Row 10: P1, [P2tog, P8 (10), P2tog tbl, P1] twice.

Row 11: K1, [SSK, K6 (8), K2tog, K1] twice.

Row 12: P1, [P2tog, P4 (6), P2tog tbl, P1] twice.

Row 13: K1, [SSK, K2 (4), K2tog, K1] twice.

Row 14: P1, [P2tog, P0 (2), P2tog tbl, P1] twice.

Row 15, Size L only: P1, (P2tog, P2tog tbl) twice.

All sizes: Cut yarn and thread through rem sts; pull tight and sew side seam. With CC tail, sew picot-edge hem.

Finishing

Block mitten.

Make 1 flower and 2 leaves as for sweater (see pages 89–90) and attach to front of mitten.**

Left Mitten

Work cuff to thumb rows 14 (16) as for right mitten.

Thumb Increases

Row 1: K19 (20), PM, M1, K2, M1, PM, K21 (23).

Row 2: Purl.

Row 3: K19 (20), M1, K4, M1, K21 (23).

Row 4: Purl.

Row 5: K19 (20), M1, K6, M1, K21 (23).

Row 6: Purl.

Rows 7–14 (16): Cont inc as set on alternate rows for a total of 16 (18) sts between markers.

Row 15 (17): Work thumb: K35 (39), turn, CO 1 st, P16 (18), turn, CO 1 st, K17 (19).

Cont as established between ** to ** on right mitten for thumb, top shaping, and finishing.

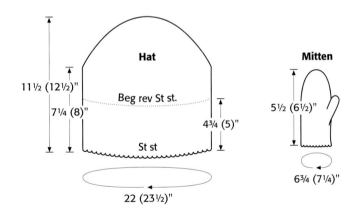

Evening Jacket

This jacket features a romantic, shaped silhouette with flowers
and a picot edge decorating the hem and bell-shaped cuffs.

Knitted Measurements

Adult Sizes: Small (Medium, Large)
Shown in size Small

Bust: 39 (41, 44½)"
Length: 20½ (21¼, 22)"

Materials

- 6 (7, 7) hanks Hifa Bomullsgarn (100% mercerized cotton; 100g, 227yds per hank), color 345 Rose, or other fingering-weight yarn
- 1 hank Hifa Bomullsgarn, color 347 Chocolate, or other fingering-weight yarn
- Size 1 US (2.5mm) circular needle
- Size 2 US (3mm) circular needle or size required to obtain gauge
- Stitch markers
- 9 buttons, 7/16" diameter

Gauge

33 sts and 35 rows = 4" in stranded knitting on size 2 needle

32 sts and 40 rows = 4" in plain stockinette stitch on size 1 needle

NOTE: You will not need to weave in the long floats of the stranded knitting because they will be covered with a facing.

Back

With size 1 needle and Rose, CO 140 (150, 162) sts. Working in St st, inc 1 st at each edge every 7 rows 4 times—148 (158, 170) sts. Work until 35 rows are completed. On row 36 (WS), evenly inc 4 sts—152 (162, 174) sts. Change to size 2 needle. **Picot row:** *YO, K2tog, rep from * to end. **Next row:** YO, purl to end, and inc 1 st—154 (164, 176) sts. Beg back chart, working color and shaping. At end of back chart, change to size 1 needle. On next WS row, evenly dec 6 sts—140 (150, 162) sts. Work in St st for 2", then inc 1 st at each edge every 6 (7, 7) rows 8 (8, 9) times—156 (166, 180) sts. Work even until piece measures 11 (11¾, 12¼)" from YO-K2tog row, ending with completed WS row.

Armhole Shaping

At each edge, BO 5 sts once, 3 sts twice, 2 sts 2 (2, 3) times, and 1 st 4 (6, 9) times—118 (124, 130) sts. Work even until armhole measures 9½ (9½, 9¾)", ending with completed WS row.

Shoulder and Neck Shaping

Next row (RS), BO 8 (8, 9) sts, work across 33 (35, 36) sts, BO center 36 (38, 38) sts, finish row. **Turn and work this side first:** At side edge, BO 8 (8, 9) sts twice, 8 (9, 9) sts twice; AT SAME TIME at neck edge, BO 5 sts once and 4 sts once. **On WS, attach yarn at neck edge and work opposite side as follows:** At neck edge, BO 5 sts once, 4 sts once; AT SAME TIME at side edge, BO 8 (8, 9) sts once and 8 (9, 9) sts twice.

Left Front

With size 1 needle and Rose, CO 70 (74, 80) sts. Working in St st, on outside edge only, inc 1 st every 7 rows 4 times—74 (78, 84) sts. Work until 35 rows are completed. On row 36 (WS), evenly inc 2 sts—76 (80, 86) sts. Change to size 2 needle. **Picot row:** *YO, K2tog, rep from * to end. **Next row:** YO, purl to end; for size Small only, dec 1 st—76 (81, 87) sts. Beg left front chart, working color and shaping. Change to size 1 needle. On next row (WS), evenly dec

2 sts—70 (75, 81) sts. Work St st for 2", then inc 1 st on outside edge every 6 (7, 7) rows 8 (8, 9) times—78 (83, 90) sts. Work even until piece measures 11 (11¾, 12¼)" from YO-K2tog row, ending with completed WS row.

Armhole Shaping

At armhole edge, BO 5 sts once, 3 sts twice, 2 sts 2 (2, 3) times, and 1 st 4 (6, 9) times—59 (62, 65) sts. Work even until piece measures 15¾ (16¼, 17)" from YO-K2tog row, ending with completed RS row.

V-Neck Shaping

At neck edge, BO 2 sts 5 times, 1 st 15 (16, 16) times, then 1 st every other neck edge 2 times—32 (34, 36) sts. Work even until same length as back (just a few rows to go), then shape shoulders as for back.

Right Front

Work as for left front, reversing shaping and following right front chart.

Sleeves (Make 2)

With size 1 needle and Rose, CO 63 sts. Work in St st for 36 rows as follows: inc 1 st at each edge every 7 rows 4 times; AT SAME TIME on row 1, inc 9 sts evenly across row. On rows 10 and 21, inc 8 sts evenly across row. On row 36 (WS), inc 2 sts evenly across row—98 sts. Change to size 2 needle. **Picot row:** *YO, K2tog, rep from * to end. **Next row:** YO, purl to end—99 sts. **Next row (WS):** dec 3 sts evenly across row. Beg cuff chart, working color and shaping—64 sts. At end of cuff chart, change to size 1 needle. Work in St st for 3 (2¾, 2)", then inc 1 st at each edge every 3 rows 29 (31, 33) times—122 (126, 130) sts. Work even until sleeve length measures 17¼" from YO-K2tog row, ending with completed WS row.

Cap Shaping

At each edge, BO 5 sts once, 3 sts twice, 2 sts 2 (2, 3) times, 1 st 4 (8, 8) times. BO 1 st every fourth row 5 (3, 5) times. At each edge, BO 1 st 10 (10, 6) times, 2 sts 4 (4, 5) times, 3 sts twice, and 4 sts twice. BO rem 10 sts.

Finishing

Block pieces to measurements. Sew shoulders and side seams. Split plies of yarn and sew facing with 1 ply through backs of sts, being careful not to go all the way through to the front.

Neck and Bottom Band

With size 1 needle and rose, start at right front and PU 108 (112, 117) sts, PM, PU 54 (61, 61) sts along right V neck, 35 (37, 37) sts along back, 54 (61, 61) sts along left V neck, PM, PU 108 (112, 117) sts along left front—359 (383, 393) sts. Mark placement for 9 buttons on left band, with first and last buttons ¼" from top and bottom. Work 7 rows in garter st (purl 1 row, knit 1 row); AT SAME TIME on RS rows, inc 1 st at markers. On row 4 of right band, work 9 buttonholes to correspond with button placement by working YO, K2tog. Sew on buttons.

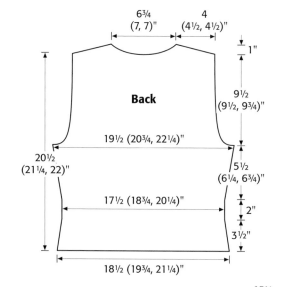

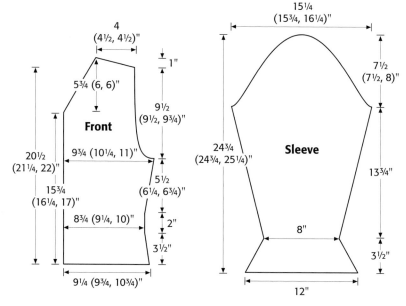

Back

Pattern continues along this line.

Center back

29 27 25 23 21 19 17 15 13 11 9 7 5 3 1

L M S

Pattern continues along this line.

Center back

28 26 24 22 20 18 16 14 12 10 8 6 4 2

L M S

Right Front

Left Front

Cuff
All sizes

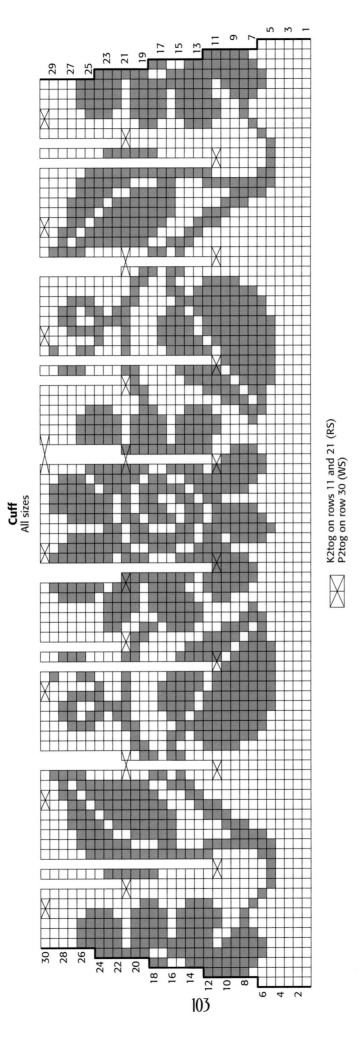

K2tog on rows 11 and 21 (RS)
P2tog on row 30 (WS)

103

Evening Bodice

This bodice or vest matches the evening jacket and features a shaped silhouette and a center panel of flowers.

Knitted Measurements

Adult Sizes: Small (Medium, Large)
Shown in size Small

Bust: 36 (38½, 41)"
Length: 17½ (17¾, 18½)"

Materials

- 3 (4, 4) hanks Hifa Bomullsgarn (100% mercerized cotton; 100g, 227yds per hank), color 345 Rose, or other fingering-weight yarn
- 1 hank Hifa Bomullsgarn, color 347 Chocolate, or other fingering-weight yarn
- Size 1 US (2.5mm) circular needle
- Size 2 US (3mm) circular needle or size required to obtain gauge
- Stitch holders
- Stitch markers

Gauge

33 sts and 35 rows = 4" in stranded knitting on size 2 needle

32 sts and 40 rows = 4" in plain stockinette stitch on size 1 needle

NOTE: To avoid the dimpling that can occur with weaving, I did not weave in the long floats of the stranded knitting.

Back

With size 1 needle and Rose, CO 124 (132, 136) sts. Work in St st for 1", ending with completed WS row. **Picot edge:** *YO, K2tog, rep from * to end. **Next row:** YO, purl across to last 2 sts, K2tog. Work even until piece measures 4¼" from YO-K2tog row. At each side

edge, inc 1 st every 4 (4, 3) rows 10 (11, 14) times. Work even until piece measures 8¾ (9, 9½)" from YO-K2tog row, ending with completed WS row.

Armhole Shaping

At each edge, BO 5 sts once, 3 sts twice, 2 sts 2 (2, 3) times, 1 st 7 (10, 10) times—100 (104, 110) sts. Work even until piece measures 14¾ (15¼, 16)" from YO-K2tog row, ending with completed WS row.

Neck and Left Shoulder Shaping

K18 (19, 21) sts, place center 64 (66, 68) sts on holder, work even on left shoulder until piece measures 17½ (17¾, 18½)" from YO-K2tog row, ending with completed WS row. At outer edge, BO 9 (10, 11) sts once and 9 (9, 10) sts once.

Right Shoulder Shaping

Attach yarn at neck edge on WS and work right shoulder as for left shoulder, reversing shaping.

Center Front

With size 1 needle and Rose, CO 58 (60, 62) sts. Work in St st for 1", ending with completed WS row. Change to size 2 needle. **Picot edge:** *YO, K2tog, rep from * to end. **Next row:** YO, purl across to last 2 sts, K2tog. Beg chart, working color changes and shaping. When finished with graph, place sts on holder.

Left Side Front

With size 1 needle and Rose, CO 36 (39, 40) sts. Work in St st for 1", ending with completed WS row. **Picot edge:** *YO, K2tog, rep from * to end. **Next row:** YO, purl across to last 2 sts, K2tog. Work even until piece measures 4¼" from YO-K2tog row, ending with completed WS row. Inc at outside edge as for back; AT SAME TIME, dec inside edge as follows: Dec 1 st every 12 rows 6 times. When piece measures 8¾ (9, 9½)" from YO-K2tog row, ending with completed WS row, start armhole shaping.

Armhole Shaping

At outside edge, BO 5 sts once, 3 sts twice, 2 sts 2 (2, 3) times, 1 st 7 (10, 10) times—18 (19, 21) sts. Work even until piece measures 17½ (17¾, 18½)" from YO-K2tog row, ending with completed WS row.

Shoulder Shaping

At outside edge, BO 9 (10, 11) sts once and 9 (9, 10) sts once.

Right Side Front

Work as for left side front, reversing shaping.

Finishing

Block pieces to measurements. Sew side fronts to center front. Sew shoulders and side seams. Split plies of yarn and sew facing with 1 ply through backs of sts, being careful not to go all the way through to the front.

Neckband

With size 1 needle and Rose, start at right back shoulder and PU 20 (21, 22) sts, PM, K64 (66, 68) sts from center back holder, PM, PU 20 (21, 22) sts across left back, 36 (37, 38) sts along left front, PM, PU center front sts off holder as follows: K2tog, knit across to last 2 sts, SSK, PM, PU 36 (37, 38) sts up right front—244 (252, 260) sts. Purl 1 row. (Knit 1 row, purl 1 row) 3 times; AT SAME TIME, **dec on knit rows at markers as follows:** SSK before a marker and K2tog after marker.

Armhole Bands

With size 1 needle and Rose, PU 128 (134, 140) sts. Purl 1 row. (Knit 1 row, purl 1 row) 3 times. BO in patt.

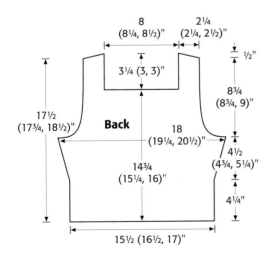

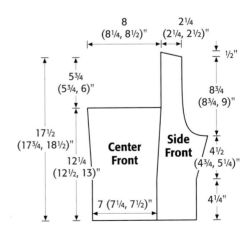

Pattern continues along this line.

Pattern continues along this line.

Bottom

Traditional Floral Cardigan

Traditional shaping and a simple pattern repeat make this relaxed cardigan a fun one to make. A colorful lower band and picot edging finish off the garment.

Knitted Measurements

Adult Sizes: Small (Medium, Large, X-Large)
Shown in size Small

Bust: 38 (42, 45, 48)"
Length: 23 (23½, 23½, 24)"

Materials

- Rauma Finullgarn (100% wool; 50g, 180yds per ball), or other 2-ply yarn, in the following amounts and colors:

7 (8, 8, 9) balls	435 Red
4 (4, 5, 5) balls	401 White
1 (2, 2, 2) balls	482 Blue
1 ball	432 Dark Green
1 ball	489 Light Green
1 ball	417 Gold

- Sizes 1 US (2.5mm) circular needle or size required to obtain gauge
- Size 2 US (3mm) circular needle
- Stitch markers
- Stitch holders
- 7 buttons, ¾" diameter

Gauge

30 sts and 36 rows = 4" in stranded knitting on size 1 needle

Body

With size 1 needle and Red, CO 286 (310, 334, 358) sts. Knit 6 rows in St st. Change to size 2 needle. **Picot edge (RS):** *YO, K2tog, rep from * to end. **Next row:** YO, purl to end. You will gain 1 st. Beg row 1 of chart and PM as follows: K71 (77, 83, 89) sts, PM, K1, PM, K143 (155, 167, 179) sts, PM, K1, PM, K71 (77, 83, 89) sts. The st between markers is center underarm st. Follow front and back chart for color and shaping to beg of armhole.

Armhole Shaping

Following in patt, K69 (75, 81, 87) sts and place on holder, BO 5 sts, K139 (151, 163, 175) sts, BO 5 sts, K69 (75, 81, 87) sts and place on holder. Working back and forth, follow back chart for color and shaping.

Left Front

Pick up sts for left front and follow left front chart for color and shaping.

Right Front

Pick up sts for right front and follow right front chart for color and shaping.

Sleeves (Make 2)

With size 1 needle and Red, CO 59 (63, 63, 67) sts. Work in K1, P1 rib for 1½". Change to size 2 needle. Working from sleeve chart, inc 1 st at each side EOR 6 (7, 7, 8) times and 1 st at each side every 5 rows 28 (29, 29, 30) times—127 (135, 135, 143) sts. Work even until sleeve measures 21 (21¼, 21¼, 21¼)".

Cap Shaping

BO 2 sts at beg of next 12 rows, then 1 st at beg of next 2 rows. BO rem 101 (109, 109, 117) sts.

Finishing

Block pieces to measurements. Sew or work 3-needle BO to join shoulders. Fold picot edge at YO row and sew hem in place.

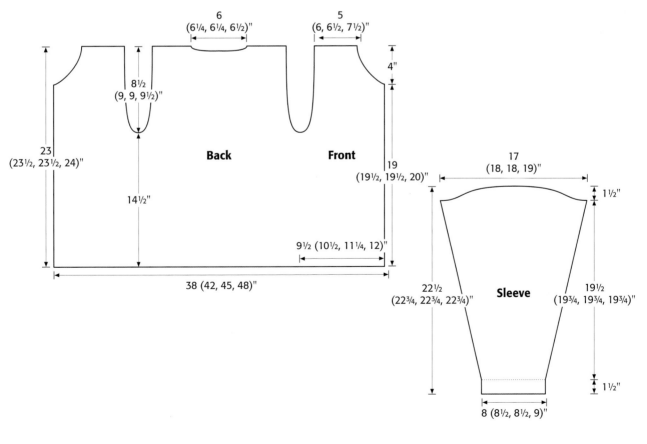

6
(6¼, 6¼, 6½)"

5
(6, 6½, 7½)"

4"

8½
(9, 9, 9½)"

23
(23½, 23½, 24)"

Back

Front

19
(19½, 19½, 20)"

14½"

9½ (10½, 11¼, 12)"

38 (42, 45, 48)"

17
(18, 18, 19)"

1½"

Sleeve

22½
(22¾, 22¾, 22¾)"

19½
(19¾, 19¾, 19¾)"

1½"

8 (8½, 8½, 9)"

Sleeve

12-stitch repeat

S | M, L | XL

Collar

With size 1 needle and Red, PU 36 (38, 38, 40) sts on right front, 47 (49, 49, 51) sts across back, 36 (38, 38, 40) sts on left front—119 (125, 125, 131) sts. Work in K1, P1 rib for 1". BO in patt.

Left and Right Bands

With size 1 needle and Red, PU 155 (159, 159, 163) sts on left front. Work in K1, P1 rib for 1". BO in patt. Make right buttonhole band to correspond with left button band. Make 7 buttonholes evenly spaced, with the first and last buttonholes ¾" from top and bottom edges. BO 3 sts for each buttonhole and CO 3 sts on return row.

Sew sleeve seams. Set sleeves into armholes. Sew on buttons.

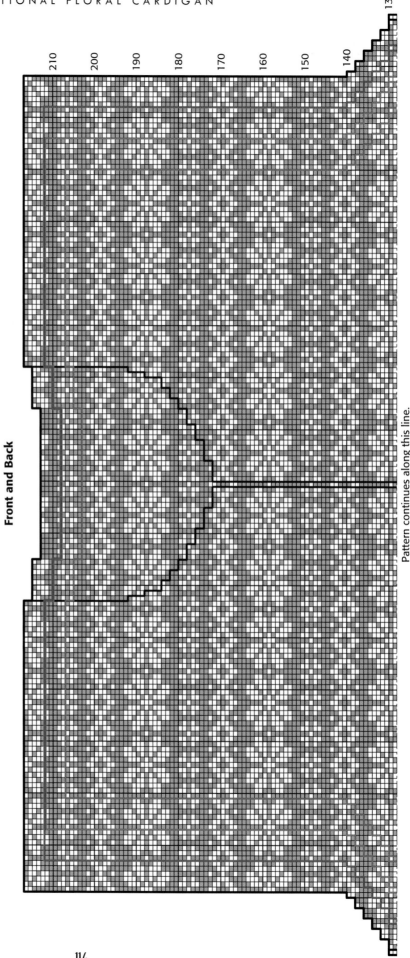

Front and Back

130 210 200 190 180 170 160 150 140

Pattern continues along this line.

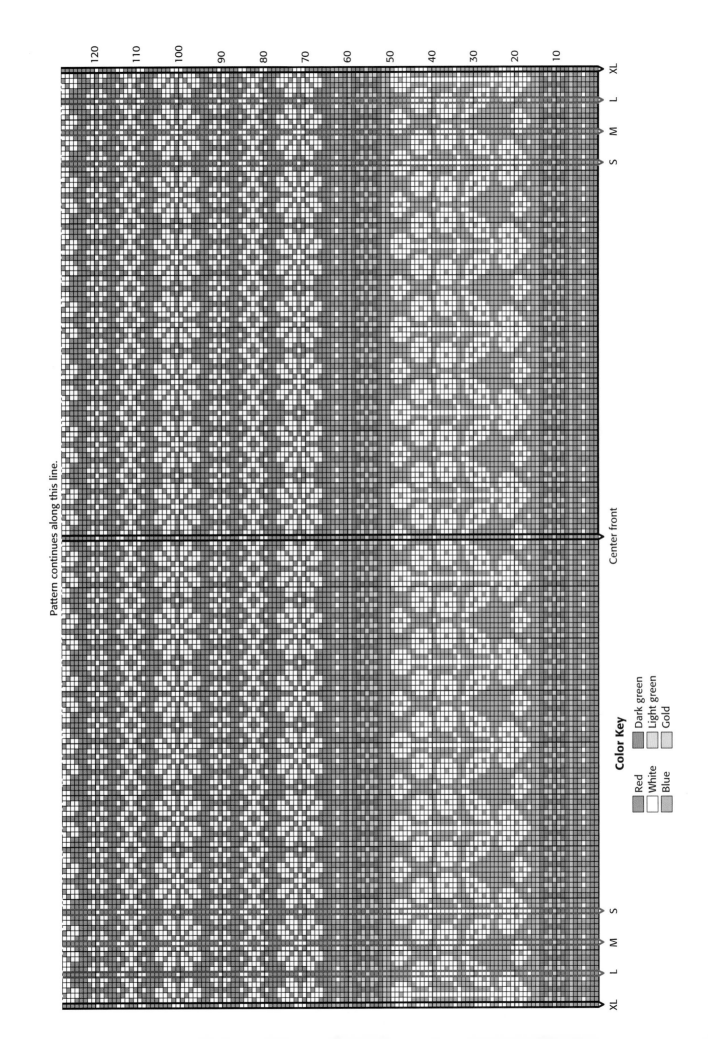

Pattern continues along this line.

Center front

Color Key

Red
White
Blue
Dark green
Light green
Gold

120 110 100 90 80 70 60 50 40 30 20 10

XL L M S

S M L XL

Butterfly Pullover

Intense stripes of color give lots of impact, while a butterfly band gives interest and playfulness to this garment. Two-color cuffs and collar pull this sweater together.

Knitted Measurements

Adult Sizes: Small (Medium, Large, X-Large)
Shown in size Small

Bust: 39 (42, 45, 48)"
Length: 21½ (22¼, 23, 24)"

Materials

- Rauma Finullgarn (100% wool; 50g, 180yds per ball), or other 2-ply yarn, in the following amounts and colors:

4 (4, 5, 5) balls	418 Red
2 (2, 3, 3) balls	499 Cinnamon
2 (2, 3, 3) balls	4886 Fuchsia
2 (2, 3, 3) balls	456 Pink
1 ball	497 Raisin
1 ball	441 Dark Plum
1 ball	474 Dark Grape
1 ball	498 Green

- Size 0 US (2mm) circular needle
- Size 1 US (2.5mm) circular needle
- Size 2 US (3mm) circular needle or size required to obtain gauge
- Stitch holders

Gauge

30 sts and 36 rows = 4" in stranded knitting on size 2 needles

29 sts and 39 rows = 4" in plain stockinette stitch on size 2 needles

Back

With size 0 needle and Cinnamon, CO 148 (158, 170, 182) sts; leave a long tail to sew hem later. Knit 10 rows even (1"), ending with completed WS row. Change to size 1 needle,

K2tog, YO, rep from * to *, end K2tog (you will lose 1 st)—147 (157, 169, 181) sts. Knit 3 rows even, then change to Red for 1 row. Change to size 2 needle. Work all rows from chart. On last row of chart (Dark Grape row), evenly dec 6 sts—141 (151, 163, 175) sts. Work in stripe sequence until piece measures 14 (14¼, 14½, 15)" from YO-K2tog row, ending with completed WS row.

Stripe sequence:

8 rows	Red
1 row	Cinnamon
5 rows	Pink
3 rows	Cinnamon
6 rows	Fuchsia

Armhole Shaping

Cont in stripe sequence, at beg of each row, BO 3 sts 4 times, 2 sts 4 times, and 1 st 6 (10, 10, 10) times—115 (121, 133 145) sts. Work even until piece measures 20¾ (21½, 22¼, 23¼)" from YO-K2tog row, ending with completed WS row.

Neck and Shoulder Shaping

K37 (40, 44, 48) sts; attach second ball of yarn and BO center 41 (41, 45, 49) sts, finish row. Working both sides at once, at each neck edge, BO 5 sts once, then 3 sts once. Work 3 rows even. BO rem 29 (32, 36, 40) sts.

Front

Work as for back (including armhole shaping) until piece measures 17½ (17¾, 18, 18¾)" from YO-K2tog row, ending with completed WS row—115 (121, 133, 145) sts.

Neck and Shoulder Shaping

K47 (50, 55, 60) sts, put center 21 (21, 23, 25)

sts on holder, join second ball of yarn, K47 (50, 55, 60) rem sts. Working both sides at once, at each neck edge, BO 4 sts once, 3 sts once, 2 sts twice, 1 st 3 times, then 1 st EOR 4 (4, 5, 6) times. Work even until piece measures the same as back. BO rem 29 (32, 36, 40) sts for each shoulder.

Sleeves (Make 2)

With size 2 needle and Cinnamon, CO 71 (71, 75, 75) sts. Add Red and work two-color ribbing as follows: **Row 1 (RS):** *K3 with Red, P1 with Cinnamon*, rep from * to *, end K3 with Red. **Row 2 (WS):** Purl the purl sts, knit the knit sts, matching the colors as established. Work rib for 2 (2, 1¾, 1¾)". Work in St st in

stripe sequence as follows:

    1 row Cinnamon

    5 rows Pink

    3 rows Cinnamon

    6 rows Fuchsia

    8 rows Red

AT SAME TIME, inc 1 st at each side every 8 (7, 6, 5) rows 19 (22, 24, 28) times—109 (115, 123, 131) sts. Work even until piece measures 20¼ (20¼, 20½, 20½)".

Cap Shaping

At each edge, BO 3 sts twice, 2 sts twice, 1 st 3 (5, 5, 5) times. BO rem 83 (85, 93, 101) sts.

Finishing

Block pieces to measurements. Sew shoulders and side seams. Sew picot hem.

Neckband

With RS facing, size 2 needle, and Cinnamon, start at right back seam and PU 79 (79, 83, 87) sts across back, 30 (34, 39, 44) sts across right front, K21 (21, 23, 25) sts from holder, PU 30 (34, 39, 44) sts across left front—160 (168, 184, 200) sts. Add red and work two-color rib as for sleeves. Cont in patt until neckband measures 1½". BO loosely with Cinnamon.

Sew sleeve seams. Set sleeves into armholes.

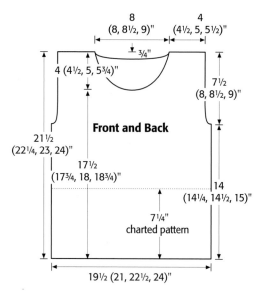

Front and Back

8 (8, 8½, 9)"

4 (4½, 5, 5½)"

¾"

4 (4½, 5, 5¾)"

7½ (8, 8½, 9)"

21½ (22¼, 23, 24)"

17½ (17¾, 18, 18¾)"

14 (14¼, 14½, 15)"

7¼" charted pattern

19½ (21, 22½, 24)"

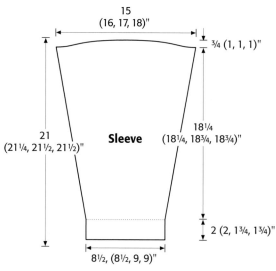

Sleeve

15 (16, 17, 18)"

¾ (1, 1, 1)"

21 (21¼, 21½, 21½)"

18¼ (18¼, 18¾, 18¾)"

2 (2, 1¾, 1¾)"

8½, (8½, 9, 9)"

Color Key

Dark grape	Red
Green	Raisin
Dark plum	Cinnamon

Knitting Terms and Abbreviations

approx . . . . . . approximate

beg . . . . begin(ning)

BO . . . . bind off

CC . . . . contrasting color

CO . . . . cast on

cont . . . . continue

dec . . . . decrease

dpn . . . . double-pointed needles

EOR . . . . every other row

inc . . . . increase

K . . . . knit

K2tog . . . . . . knit two together

K2tog tbl . . . . knit two together through
back loops

M1 . . . . increase one stitch

MC . . . . main color

P . . . . purl

P2sso . . . . pass two slip stitches over

P2tog . . . . . . purl two together

P2tog tbl . . . . purl two together through
back loops

PM . . . . place marker

psso . . . . pass slip stitch over

PU . . . . pick up

rem . . . . remaining

RS . . . . right side

sl . . . . slip

SSK . . . . slip, slip, knit two stitches
together

st(s) . . . . stitch(es)

St st . . . . stockinette stitch

tog . . . . together

WS . . . . wrong side

YO . . . . yarn over

Knitting Techniques

Refer to this section when you want to brush up on knitting techniques. You'll find casting on, binding off, color work, intarsia, and more.

Casting On

The following two cast-on methods are handy for the projects in this book.

Cable Cast On

This is my preferred cast on for most garments. I specifically request this cast on for some designs because of its decorative edge. Start with a slipknot on your left needle. Insert right needle into slipknot as if to knit and pull stitch through and place it on left needle. Next, *insert right needle between stitches and pull stitch through and place on left needle*; repeat from * to * for the amount of stitches needed.

Insert needle between two stitches. Knit a stitch.

Place new stitch on left needle.

Thumb Cast On

This is one of the most basic cast ons and usually the first one learned. Wrap yarn around thumb as illustrated and insert needle upward though loop and pull off thumb. Repeat this motion for the amount of stitches needed. I sometimes use this cast on to make an increase or to make the return stitches on a buttonhole.

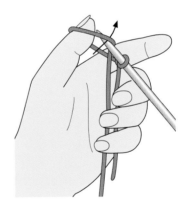

Binding Off

For binding off, use whichever of the following methods that best suits your needs.

Three-Needle Bind Off

This bind off is great for shoulder seams and I use a variation of this bind off for the vein of a three-dimensional leaf. The instructions throughout the book say to bind off shoulders, but if instead you put them onto holders, block your pieces, and then put your stitches back onto needles, you can use this bind off. Place the front stitches on one needle, and the back stitches on a second needle. With right sides facing, use a third needle to knit the front and back together as follows: Insert the right needle into the first stitches on the needles in your left hand, as if to knit. Knit the two stitches together at the same time. Repeat this step for the second stitches from each needle, giving you two stitches on the right needle. Then bind off the first stitch by passing it over the second stitch. Continue as established until only one stitch is left; cut yarn and pull through.

Knit together one stitch from front needle and one stitch from back needle.

Bind off.

Sewn Bind Off

This bind off is a close match to the cable cast on and is very flexible. You will need a tapestry needle and a tail five times the length of the area to be bound off. Insert needle into second stitch as if to knit and pull through to the back; then coming forward, insert the needle into first stitch as if to purl, pull through, going

under the new loop being made. Slip first stitch off and pull yarn to neaten. Continue until all stitches are bound off.

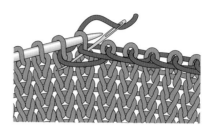

Color Work

Stranded and Intarsia knitting are two common ways of adding color to a garment.

Stranded Knitting

In stranded knitting, you will follow a chart and loosely carry the unused yarn on the wrong side of your work. Also called Fair Isle, this technique uses two colors per row and is worked with one color held in each hand. If you put your background color in your right hand and your motif color in your left hand, the motif will show more. It has to do with the path the yarn takes; you can read up on this in some of my recommended reference books. When stranding with a finer-weight wool, skip no more than five to seven stitches without weaving (or catching) the float; you do not want your fingers to catch in the float.

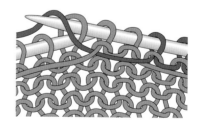

Intarsia

Intarsia uses many colors, but the colors do not travel from one edge to the other as in stranded knitting. It is best to work with shorter lengths of yarn or wrap longer lengths of yarn into butterflies (I would avoid plastic holders). That way, if you need to untangle them, it's much easier. Always twist yarns to avoid holes.

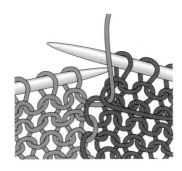

I-Cord

Using double-pointed needles, cast on three stitches (or whatever pattern calls for) and *knit three stitches, slide stitches to the other end of needle, and knit three stitches again*, rep from * to *. A tube will start forming. Do not worry about the float that occurs in the back; when your I-cord is the desired length, give it a good pull and the float will disappear.

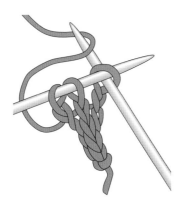

M1

M1 means to make 1 stitch. With right-hand needle, lift the ladder or bar between two stitches and place it on left-hand needle; knit into the back of the stitch.

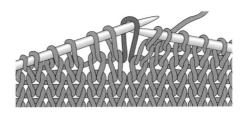

Ladder Stitch

Also known as mattress stitch, the ladder stitch is a great way to finish side seams or sleeves. Place the pieces to be seamed next to each other with right sides facing up. Insert the needle under the horizontal bar between two stitches on the left piece, and then repeat with the matching row on the right piece. Continue weaving back and forth until the seam is completed. Make sure to pull tight every five stitches or so to keep the stitches neat, but do not pull too tightly as this will gather the edge. I like to pull snugly and then slightly stretch out the seam.

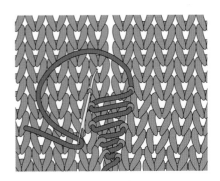

Yarn Resources

For a list of shops in your area that carry the yarns mentioned in this book, contact the following companies.

Nordic Fiber Arts
(supplier of Rauma and Hifa yarns)
4 Cutts Rd.
Durham, NH 03824
Phone: 603-868-1196
Web site: www.nordicfiberarts.com
Email: info@nordicfiberarts.com

Berroco Yarns
PO Box 367
Uxbridge, MA 01569
Toll-free: 800-343-4948
Web site: www.berroco.com
Email: info@berroco.com

Dale of Norway
N 16 W. 23390 Stoneridge Dr., Ste. A
Waukesha, WI 53188
Toll-free: 800-441-DALE (3253)
Web site: www.dale.no

Haneke Wool Fashions
630 N. Black Cat Rd.
Meridian, ID 83642
Toll-free: 800-523-WOOL (9665)

Reference Books

Allen, Pam. *Knitting for Dummies.* New York: Hungry Minds, Inc., 2002.

Feitelson, Ann. *The Art of Fair Isle Knitting.* Loveland, Colo.: Interweave Press, 1996.

Stanley, Montse. *Reader's Digest Knitter's Handbook.* Pleasantville, N. Y.: The Reader's Digest Associations, Inc., 1993.

Starmore, Alice. *Alice Starmore's Book of Fair Isle Knitting.* Newton, Conn.: The Taunton Press, 1988.

Thomas, Mary. *Mary Thomas's Knitting Book.* New York: Dover Publications, Inc., 1972.

new and bestselling titles from

America's Best-Loved Knitting Books®

America's Best-Loved Quilt Books®

NEW RELEASES
20 Decorated Baskets
Asian Elegance
Batiks and Beyond
Classic Knitted Vests
Clever Quilts Encore
Crocheted Socks!
Four Seasons of Quilts
Happy Endings
Judy Murrah's Jacket Jackpot
Knits for Children and Their Teddies
Loving Stitches
Meadowbrook Quilts
Once More around the Block
Pairing Up
Patchwork Memories
Pretty and Posh
Professional Machine Quilting
Purely Primitive
Shadow Appliqué
Snowflake Follies
Style at Large
Trashformations
World of Quilts, A

APPLIQUÉ
Appliquilt in the Cabin
Artful Album Quilts
Blossoms in Winter
Color-Blend Appliqué
Garden Party
Sunbonnet Sue All through the Year

HOLIDAY QUILTS & CRAFTS
Christmas Cats and Dogs
Christmas Delights
Creepy Crafty Halloween
Handcrafted Christmas, A
Hocus Pocus!
Make Room for Christmas Quilts
Snowman's Family Album Quilt, A
Welcome to the North Pole

LEARNING TO QUILT
101 Fabulous Rotary-Cut Quilts
Casual Quilter, The
Fat Quarter Quilts
More Fat Quarter Quilts
Quick Watercolor Quilts
Quilts from Aunt Amy
Simple Joys of Quilting, The
Your First Quilt Book (or it should be!)

PAPER PIECING
40 Bright and Bold Paper-Pieced Blocks
50 Fabulous Paper-Pieced Stars
Down in the Valley
Easy Machine Paper Piecing
For the Birds
It's Raining Cats and Dogs
Papers for Foundation Piecing
Quilter's Ark, A
Show Me How to Paper Piece
Traditional Quilts to Paper Piece

QUILTS FOR BABIES & CHILDREN
Easy Paper-Pieced Baby Quilts
Even More Quilts for Baby
More Quilts for Baby
Play Quilts
Quilts for Baby
Sweet and Simple Baby Quilts

ROTARY CUTTING/SPEED PIECING
101 Fabulous Rotary-Cut Quilts
365 Quilt Blocks a Year Perpetual Calendar
1000 Great Quilt Blocks
Around the Block Again
Around the Block with Judy Hopkins
Cutting Corners
Log Cabin Fever
Pairing Up
Strips and Strings
Triangle-Free Quilts
Triangle Tricks

SCRAP QUILTS
Nickel Quilts
Rich Traditions
Scrap Frenzy
Spectacular Scraps
Successful Scrap Quilts

TOPICS IN QUILTMAKING
Americana Quilts
Bed and Breakfast Quilts
Bright Quilts from Down Under
Creative Machine Stitching
Everyday Embellishments
Fabulous Quilts from Favorite Patterns
Folk Art Friends
Handprint Quilts
Just Can't Cut It!
Quilter's Home: Winter, The
Split-Diamond Dazzlers
Time to Quilt

CRAFTS
300 Papermaking Recipes
ABCs of Making Teddy Bears, The
Blissful Bath, The
Creating with Paint
Handcrafted Frames
Handcrafted Garden Accents
Painted Whimsies
Pretty and Posh
Sassy Cats
Stamp in Color

KNITTING & CROCHET
365 Knitting Stitches a Year
    Perpetual Calendar
Basically Brilliant Knits
Crochet for Tots
Crocheted Aran Sweaters
Knitted Sweaters for Every Season
Knitted Throws and More
Knitter's Template, A
Knitting with Novelty Yarns
More Paintbox Knits
Simply Beautiful Sweaters for Men
Today's Crochet
Too Cute! Cotton Knits for Toddlers
Treasury of Rowan Knits, A
Ultimate Knitter's Guide, The